Food Tab

Oxford University Press

Oxford University Press, Great Clarendon Street, Oxford OX2 6DP

Oxford New York
Athens Auckland Bangkok Bogota Buenos Aires
Calcutta Cape Town Chennai Dar es Salaam
Delhi Florence Hong Kong Istanbul Karachi
Kuala Lumpur Madrid Melbourne Mexico City
Mumbai Nairobi Paris São Paolo Singapore
Taipei Tokyo Toronto Warsaw

and associated companies in
Berlin Ibadan

Oxford is a trade mark of Oxford University Press

© Oxford University Press 1986

Reprinted 1986 (three times), 1987 (twice), 1988, 1989, 1991, 1992
1993 (twice), 1994, 1995, 1996, 1997, 1998

ISBN 0 19 832724 2

Typeset by HiTech Typesetters Ltd, Oxford
Printed in Hong Kong

Contents

Preface

This book provides a straightforward guide to the composition of fresh and manufactured foods. These food tables will be of value to teachers, college students, and school pupils. They may be used to support work in home economics, biology, and other subjects which involve nutrition. Added to the tables are brief notes on their use, on the nutrients, and on methods of calculation. A selection of specimen calculations and sample questions is also included.

This reprint incorporates the 1991 Department of Health/MAFF Reference Nutrient Intakes.

More comprehensive background details will be found in *The Value of Food* by Patty Fisher and Arnold Bender (Oxford, 1979).

Three computer programs are available to accompany this book, permitting calculation of the nutrient yields of foods and comparison of diets with Reference Nutrient Intakes; identification of foods which are especially rich or poor sources of individual nutrients; and calculation of energy and protein requirements and the basis of Reference Nutrient Intakes. All three programs are available for either Acorn/ BBC or PC compatible computers, from Dr David A. Bender, Department of Biochemistry, University College London, Gower Street, London WC1E 6BT.

The use of food composition tables

Precision of data

Food composition tables are widely used to assess nutrient and energy intakes, and to plan meals and food supplies, as well as in the treatment of certain diseases. The composition of food can vary widely, depending, among other factors, on the variety of plant or animal, on growing and feeding conditions and, for some foods, on freshness. Hence, the tables are based on average values from a number of samples analysed in the laboratory. They must always provide *only a rough guide*, since the food under investigation cannot be the same sample as that analysed originally. For this and other reasons there are often considerable differences between the figures given in tables compiled in different countries, and they must be taken as only approximate rather than precise values.

If very accurate information is required, as in some areas of research, then it is necessary to weigh all foods eaten and to analyse them in the laboratory. This is so lengthy and expensive a procedure that it is usual practice to replace the analysis by using food composition tables.

Because of the errors mentioned above, it is never possible to obtain exact figures, and it is likely that there will be an error of ± 10% compared with the true (analysed) values – and the figures for the vitamins may be even more unreliable.

This is, however, the best that can be achieved, and it is likely that even greater errors have been introduced in assessing the amount of each food eaten, depending on the method used.

Because of these errors, it would be pointless and misleading to quote precise figures, and all those given in this book have been rounded off to provide reasonable average values. The same rounding off procedure should be carried out when calculating energy and nutrient content of meals. For example, if the total energy intake for a week comes to say 15,080 kcal, this is 2154.3 kcal/day. This figure is impossibly precise, and could not be achieved even if all the food had been analysed chemically. It should be rounded off to 2150 kcal. Note however that the rounding off should be done at the *end* of a series of calculations, otherwise rounding errors may accumulate.

For simplicity of use, only a limited number of the more common foods have been listed in the following tables, and only a limited number of nutrients. Information on additional foods, and a wider range of nutrients, will be found in: McCance and Widdowson's *The Composition of Foods* by A.A. Paul and D.A.T. Southgate (Her Majesty's Stationery Office); *Agriculture Handbook* number 8, *Composition of Foods*, United States Department of Agriculture; *Tables for Use in The Middle East* by P.L. Pellet and S. Shadarevian, American University of Beirut; and other national food composition tables. Many less common foods have never been analysed, so no figures are available anywhere.

If precise information is required about manufactured foods, then in many instances the manufacturer can provide either specific information for a given batch, or the average and range of variation of the nutrients found in very large numbers of samples analysed over the years.

SI units

In addition to the ordinary metric system, there is a relatively new, logical system of units, the Système Internationale d'Unités (SI units), which has been adopted by most scientific journals. This consists of seven basic units: length (metre), mass (kg), time (seconds), electric current (ampere), thermodynamic temperature (kelvin), luminous intensity (candela), and amount of substance (mole). Other units are derived from these basic seven.

Fractions and multiples of units are expressed as follows:

Fraction	Prefix	Symbol	Multiple	Prefix	Symbol
10^{-1}	deci	d	10	deca	da
10^{-2}	centi	c	10^2	hecto	h
10^{-3}	milli	m	10^3	kilo	k
10^{-6}	micro	μ	10^6	mega	M
10^{-9}	nano	n	10^9	giga	G
10^{-12}	pico	p	10^{12}	tera	T
10^{-15}	femto	f			

In the area of nutrition, the joule is a derived SI unit. 1 kcal = 4186.8 J, expressed as 4.2 kJ. Note that megajoule has a capital M (MJ), while kilojoule has a small k (kJ). The SI unit for pressure is the pascal, with pressures normally measured in kilopascals (kPa).

Notes on the nutrients

The food we eat must supply us with enough energy to meet our needs for normal activity (but not too much, since the excess is stored in the body as fat), enough protein to meet our needs for growth and repair, and the thirteen vitamins and twenty-five or so minerals that are essential for the normal functioning of the body.

Of the vitamins, only six are of nutritional importance, in the sense that they may be in short supply in some diets: vitamins A, B_1, B_2, niacin, and vitamins C and D. To a lesser extent, deficiency of folic acid may present problems in some sections of the community. However, the analysis of folic acid in foods, and the extent to which it is available from foods, presents problems, and accordingly folic acid is not listed in the tables. Deficiencies of the other vitamins are extremely rare.

In the same sense, calcium and iron are nutritionally important, and are listed. The sodium content is also listed, since it may be desirable to reduce our intake of sodium.

Table 17 lists the dietary fibre content of those relatively few foods that are reasonable sources, and Table 18 lists the few foods that contain significant amounts of vitamin D.

In the main table (Table 19), the foods are arranged in alphabetical order and numbered, with cross-references as appropriate. In the tables of dietary fibre (Table 17) and vitamin D (Table 18) the same numbers are used in these tables as in the main table.

Dietary fibre

This includes (1) cellulose, (2) insoluble non-cellulose polysaccharides and (3) soluble non-cellulose polysaccharides which are not digested. (1) plus (2) constitute the insoluble fibre in foods; (3) is termed soluble fibre.

Some methods of analysis include non-digestible starch ('resistant starch') and also lignin in the total of unavailable carbohydrate (although lignin is not a carbohydrate), so there are differences between some of the figures published for total dietary fibre. In order to standardise figures for labelling and regulatory purposes, the Ministry of Agriculture, Fisheries and Food has selected a method of analysis that does not include lignin and non-digestible starch. Such values are not available for all foods, and in Table 17 the total fibre content of foods is given. In view of the analytical difficulties, as well as the problems posed by the inclusion or exclusion of lignin and resistant starch, *all values shown in Table 17 must be regarded as approximate*.

Some older textbooks refer to 'crude fibre'. This is a technical analytical term, and is quite unrelated to dietary fibre.

Energy

It is correct to refer to the energy content of a food, or the energy requirements of an individual, and then to express the figures in kcal or kJ, instead of referring to the Calorie or kilojoule content or requirements.

Since Calories (best referred to as kcal) are commonly used alongside joules (the normal unit is the kilojoule, kJ) as units of energy, both are used here.

The more exact relationship between the two units is 1 kcal = 4.18 kJ, but it is usually rounded off to 1 kcal = 4.2 kJ.

Protein

The protein content of foods is usually measured by analysing for total nitrogen (by the Kjeldahl method), although foods also contain some non-protein nitrogen, then multiplying by the N conversion factor. Proteins from different sources differ in this factor: it is 5.3 for legumes, 5.7 for cereals, 6.25 for most animal proteins, and 6.38 for milk. When a mixed dish is being analysed it is usual to use the factor 6.25 – hence, protein = 6.25 × N.

Carbohydrates

Some authorities calculate carbohydrate by the difference between 100% and the measured content of protein, fat, and mineral ash. Sometimes this figure is corrected for unavailable carbohydrate (dietary fibre).

The British tables have always been derived by measuring available carbohydrate as glucose after hydrolysis of starches and sugars, and this is the way in which they are expressed in these tables. Since the hydrolysis of starch involves the addition of one molecule of water for each glucose unit produced, the total of all nutrients in a food will usually come to more than 100%, but this problem can be ignored.

Vitamin A

Vitamin A itself (retinol) is found only in foods of animal origin. However, the carotene of vegetable foods is converted to vitamin A in the body, and in these tables we have added together both retinol and carotene under the heading 'vitamin A'.

The amount of carotene that is absorbed and converted to retinol in the wall of the intestine varies with the food (for example, it is better absorbed from a purée of carrot than from whole carrots), and also with the different forms of carotene. Vitamin A in foods is expressed as *retinol equivalents* (R.E.). The carotene or other form of vitamin A is multiplied by an appropriate factor to allow for incomplete absorption and conversion to retinol. Vitamin A used to be measured in international units of biological activity (i.u.); it is now measured in micrograms (μg).

1 μg of retinol equivalent (R.E.) is equivalent to:

> 1 μg or 3.33 i.u. retinol (in old nomenclature, 3.33 i.u. vitamin A);
> 10 i.u. or 6 μg β-carotene

This carotene conversion factor is used for all foods, with the following exceptions:

(**i**) β-Carotene is so well absorbed from milk that 2 μg carotene = 1 μg R.E.

(**ii**) The forms of the vitamin in red palm oil (α-carotene) and yellow maize (cryptoxanthin) are only half as active biologically as β-carotene. Therefore 12 μg or 20 i.u. of vitamin from these sources = 1 μg R.E. See the aid to calculation on page 8.

Niacin equivalents

Niacin (nicotinic acid and nicotinamide) can be made in the body from the essential amino acid tryptophan. Some food composition tables list 'niacin equivalents' in foods, which is the sum of the niacin and $\frac{1}{60}$ of the tryptophan content. In these tables only the niacin content of the foods is shown, ignoring the contribution that tryptophan can make.

Changes on cooking

For some foods, information is included about both the raw and cooked foods. In general, the change on cooking is the result of a gain in water when foods are boiled or stewed, or the loss of water and fat when they are grilled or roasted. Obviously, frying will increase the fat content of the food, as well as reducing the water content. There is some loss of water soluble components including vitamins into the cooking water, and some destruction of vitamins B_1 and C. The amounts lost vary widely, so *the vitamin content of cooked foods quoted is only very approximate.*

Edible portions and waste

All figures given for all foods are for edible portions: waste has already been accounted for.

An aid to calculation and conversion into μg R.E.:

(i)   μg β-carotene into μg R.E. – divide by 6
(ii) i.u. β-carotene into μg R.E. – divide by 10
(iii) i.u. retinol into μg R.E. – divide by 3.33 or multiply by 0.3

Example: egg contains both carotene (30%) and retinol (70%). Figures are listed in some books in one of three ways: a) μg of each; b) i.u. of each; c) i.u. of total vitamin A activity, where carotene figures have already been converted into retinol. We need to convert all figures into μg R.E.

example a:

retinol	210 μg	210 μg R.E.	
carotene	540 μg	540/6 = 90 μg R.E.	} 300 μg R.E.

example b:

retinol	700 i.u.	700 × 0.3 = 210 μg R.E.	
carotene	900 i.u.	900/10 = 90 μg R.E.	} 300 μg R.E.

example c: (quoted as units of vitamin A activity)

retinol	700 i.u.		
carotene	300 i.u.	} 1000 i.u.	1000 × 0.3 = 300 μg R.E.

Examples of use

1   What is the metric equivalent of 2oz?
See Table 3 (page 10):
since 1 oz = 28.35 g (approximate to 30 g)
   2 oz = 56.70 g (approximate to 60 g)

2   What is the capacity in ml of 3 standard tablespoons?
See Table 6 (page 11):
since 1 tablespoon = 15 ml
   3 tablespoons = 45 ml

3   What is the upper temperature limit for frying?
See Table 9 (page 12):
The upper limit for frying is specified as 190°C or 375°F.

4   How much protein would satisfy the needs of a moderately active man of 32?
See Table 11 (page 14):
In the age group 18–34 years, the RDA is 72 g of protein per day.

5   What would be the average expected weight for a girl at age 16 and height 5' 5"?
See Table 13 (page 17):
A girl 5' 5" (65") tall weighs on average about 128 lb (9 stone 2 lb) or 58 kg.

6   How much fat is there in a McDonald's Cheeseburger?
See Table 15 (page 21):
A cheeseburger contains 14 g of fat.

7   How much dietary fibre does 5 oz of raw chickpeas contain?
See Table 17 (page 26):
100 g of chickpeas (raw) contains 15 g of fibre.
5 oz = 150g, and therefore 150 g of raw chickpeas contains 22.5 g of fibre.

8   Compare the niacin content of raw and fried mushrooms.
See Table 19 (page 38, items 283 and 284):
100 g of mushrooms (raw) contains 4.0 mg of niacin.
100 g of mushrooms (fried) contains only 3.5 mg of niacin.

Energy yields

Table 1 Energy yields of protein, carbohydrate fat, and alcohol

	kcal/g	kJ/g
protein	4	17
carbohydrate	4	16
fat	9	37
*alcohol	7	29

* This figure is for pure alcohol. It is now common practice to quote the alcohol content of beverages as g/100ml (w/v), or percentage by volume (v/v, termed degrees Gay-Lussac, GL), or percentage by weight (w/w). Until recently in the United Kingdom the proof system was used. Proof spirit contains 49.3% alcohol by weight (w/w), 57.2% by volume (v/v) and 45.2 g/100ml.

The apparent discrepancy between using 4 kcal/g for both protein and carbohydrate, and 17 and 16 respectively when expressed as kJ/g, is due to rounding off – these are the officially established factors.

Table 2 The equivalence of degrees proof spirit

degrees proof	g/100 ml	
10	4.6	(beer and cider)
20	9.1	(table wines)
30	13.6	
40	18.2	(fortified wines)
50	22.7	
60	27.2	
70	31.7	(spirits)

Weights and measures

Table 3 Equivalence of imperial and metric units

1 oz = 28.35 g (approximate to 30 g)	100 g = 3.5 oz
1 lb (16 oz) = 454 g (approximate to 450 g)	1 kg = 2.18 lb = 35 oz
1 fluid oz = 28.35 ml	1 ml = 0.035 fluid oz
1 pint (20 fluid oz) = 568 ml (approximate to 570 ml)	1 l = 35 fluid oz = 1.75 pints
1 g = 0.035 oz	

Table 4 Approximate metric equivalents of imperial weights

imperial (oz)	metric (g)	imperial (oz)	metric (g)
1	30	6	170
2	60	7	200
3	85	8	230
4	110	16 (1 lb)	450
5	140		

Table 5 Approximate imperial equivalents of metric weights (more precise equivalents are given in brackets)

metric (g)	imperial (oz)	metric (g)	imperial (oz)
10	1/3	100	3 1/2
20	2/3	120	4 (4.2)
30	1 (1.05)	150	5 (5.25)
40	1 1/2 (1.4)	200	7
50	1 3/4	250	9 (8.75)
60	2 (2.1)	300	10 1/2
70	2 1/2	400	14
80	3	450	16 (15.75)
90	3 (3.15)	500*	17 1/2 (1 lb 1 1/2 oz)

* (500 g is often called a 'metric pound')

Table 6 Approximate metric equivalents of imperial volumes

imperial (fl oz)		metric (ml)	imperial (fl oz)		metric (ml)
1		30	8		230
2		60	9		260
3		85	10	1/2 pint	280
4		110	15	3/4 pint	425
5	1/4 pint	140	20	1 pint	570
6		170	40	1 quart	1140
7		200	160	1 gallon	4500 (4.5 litres)

1 teaspoon   5 ml
(2 teaspoons = 1 dessert-spoon
2 dessert-spoons = 1 tablespoon

US equivalent:
3 teaspoons = 1 tablespoon)
1 traditional tablespoon   20 ml

standard measuring spoons:
1/2 teaspoon   2.5 ml
1 teaspoon   5 ml
1 tablespoon   15 ml

Table 7 Approximate imperial equivalents of metric volumes

metric	imperial	metric	imperial
100 ml (1 dl)	3½ fl oz	500 ml	18 fl oz
250 ml	9 fl oz	1 l	35¼ fl oz (1¾ pints)

American measures

If you use American recipes, you will find that quantities are normally quoted in cups, and half and quarter cups. The standard American cup is a measure of volume – 8 fluid oz (237 ml). The standard British cup is 10 oz.

Because solids do not all occupy the same volume, the equivalence of cups of solids is not the same:
1 cup of butter, margarine or granulated sugar contains 8 oz (230 g) by weight;
1 cup of icing sugar contains 5⅓ oz (150 g) by weight;
1 cup of flour contains 4 oz (110 g) by weight.

The American gallon is smaller than the imperial gallon, and therefore American pints and quarts are also smaller.

Table 8 Imperial and metric equivalents of American measures of volume

American	imperial	metric
1 US gallon	6.6 imp pints	3.78 l
1 US quart	32 fl oz	945 ml
1 US pint	16 fl oz	470 ml

Temperature and pressure

The metric scale of temperature is the Celsius scale (often also called the centigrade scale), shown as °C. On this scale, the freezing point of water is 0°C, and boiling point is 100°C.

Traditionally, Britain used to use the Fahrenheit scale, °F. On this scale the freezing point of water is 32°F, and boiling point is 212°F. In recent years we have changed to use the Celsius scale. Modern recipe books quote centigrade temperatures and modern electric cookers have centigrade scales, so in these tables we will refer to *centigrade* temperatures.

To convert a Fahrenheit temperature to centigrade,
subtract 32 and multiply by $\frac{5}{9}$.

To convert a centigrade temperature to Fahrenheit,
multiply by $\frac{9}{5}$ and add 32.

Electric cookers are scaled in temperature (either centigrade or Fahrenheit). Gas ovens are not so scaled, but use a Regulo scale from a low of $\frac{1}{4}$ to a high of 10 to indicate temperature.

Table 9 Equivalence of Fahrenheit and centigrade temperatures, and gas Regulo marks

Refrigerator and freezer temperatures

centigrade	Fahrenheit	centigrade	Fahrenheit
°C	°F	°C	°F
−18	0 (*** deep-freeze)	0	32 (freezing point of water)
−11	12 (** freezing compartment)	5	41 (normal refrigerator)
−4	25 (* freezing compartment)		

Cooking temperatures

gas Regulo	centigrade	Fahrenheit	gas Regulo	centigrade	Fahrenheit
	°C	°F		°C	°F
	70	150	4	180	350 (normal hot frying)
	80	175	5	190	375 (upper limit for frying)
	100	212 (boiling point of water)	6	200	400
1/4	120	225	7	220	425 ('hot' oven)
1/2	130	250	8	230	450
1	140	275	9	240	475 ('very hot' oven)
2	150	300	10	250	500
	160	310 (normal gentle frying)		270	525
3	170	325		290	550

Table 10 Temperatures achieved in pressure cooking

Pressure above atmospheric		boiling point of water	
		centigrade	Fahrenheit
pounds	kPa	°C	°F
0	0	100	212
5	35	109	228
10	70	115	240
15	100	121	250

Reference Nutrient Intakes and Dietary Reference Values

Different people, even of the same sex, age and activity, have different requirements for nutrients. From the results of experiments on volunteers, we can calculate the average requirement, and the extent to which individuals' requirements differ from this. This gives us a range which will include most people's requirements. Statistically, the range is based on a spread of 2 standard deviations on either side of the average requirement. This range includes the requirements of 95% of the population: 2.5% would be expected to have lower requirements, and 2.5% would be expected to have higher requirements. For most nutrients the range is 20% on either side of the average requirement; for protein it is 25%. The two extremes of this range are called the *Lower Reference Nutrient Intake* (LRNI) and the *Reference Nutrient Intake* (RNI).

The *Lower Reference Nutrient Intake* is the level of intake below which most people's requirements will not be met. It is therefore the intake below which we might expect deficiency to occur (although 2.5% of people have an even lower requirement).

The *Reference Nutrient Intake* is the level of intake at which almost everyone's requirement would be met. Only 2.5% of the population have a requirement higher than the RNI, and most people have lower requirements – some as much as 40% lower than the RNI. It is

important to emphasize that the RNI *do not apply to individuals, but only to population groups.* The figures are used to plan food supplies and to assess the adequacy of community and institutional diets.

For energy we use an *average* requirement, and not an RNI set at two standard deviations above the average. An energy intake above requirement not only does not confer any benefit or safety margin, but results in obesity. Energy requirements vary considerably, depending on the individual's level of physical activity and energy expenditure.

Because vitamin D is formed through the action of sunlight on skin, and this meets requirements for most people, no RNI for vitamin D is given, except for infants under 6 months (8.5 µg), children aged 6 months – 3 years (7 µg), pregnant and lactating women (10 µg) and people aged over 65 (10 µg).

The requirements for vitamins E and K, and for pantothenic acid and biotin are not well established, and so there are no RNI for these vitamins. Estimated 'safe intakes' which are more than adequate to meet requirements, are:
   Vitamin E: men above 4 mg/day, women above 3 mg/day
   Vitamin K: 1 µg/kg body weight/day (infants 10 µg/day)
   Pantothenic acid: 3–7 mg/day
   Biotin: 10–200 µg/day

Table 11 Reference Nutrient Intakes

	Energy (MJ)	Energy (kcal)	Protein (g)	Calcium (mg)	Iron (mg)	Vitamins							
						A (µg)	B₁ (mg)	B₂ (mg)	Niacin (mg)	B₆ (mg)	B₁₂ (µg)	Folate (µg)	C (mg)
Boys													
0–3 months	2.28	545	12.5	525	1.7	350	0.2	0.4	3	0.2	0.3	50	25
4–6 months	2.89	690	12.7	525	4.3	350	0.2	0.4	3	0.2	0.3	50	25
7–9 months	3.44	825	13.7	525	7.8	350	0.2	0.4	4	0.3	0.4	50	25
10–12 months	3.85	920	14.9	525	7.8	350	0.3	0.4	5	0.4	0.4	50	25
1–3 years	5.15	1230	14.5	350	6.9	400	0.5	0.6	8	0.7	0.5	70	30
4–6 years	7.16	1715	19.7	450	6.1	500	0.7	0.8	11	0.9	0.8	100	30
7–10 years	8.24	1970	28.3	550	8.7	500	0.7	1.0	12	1.0	1.0	150	30
11–14 years	9.27	2220	42.1	1000	11·3	600	0.9	1.2	15	1.2	1.2	200	35
15–18 years	11.51	2755	55.2	1000	11.3	700	1.1	1.3	18	1.5	1.5	200	40
Men													
19–50 years	10.60	2550	55.5	700	8.7	700	1.0	1.3	17	1.4	1.5	200	40
51–59 years	10.60	2550	53.3	700	8.7	700	0.9	1.3	16	1.4	1.5	200	40
60–64 years	9.93	2380	53.3	700	8.7	700	0.9	1.3	16	1.4	1.5	200	40
65–74 years	9.71	2330	53.3	700	8.7	700	0.9	1.3	16	1.4	1.5	200	40
over 75 years	8.77	2100	53.3	700	8.7	700	0.9	1.3	16	1.4	1.5	200	40

	Energy (MJ)	Energy (kcal)	Protein (g)	Calcium (mg)	Iron (mg)	Vitamins A (μg)	B₁ (mg)	B₂ (mg)	Niacin (mg)	B₆ (mg)	B₁₂ (μg)	Folate (μg)	C (mg)
Girls													
0–3 months	2.16	515	12.5	525	1.7	350	0.2	0.4	3	0.2	0.3	50	25
4–6 months	2.69	645	12.7	525	4.3	350	0.2	0.4	3	0.2	0.3	50	25
7–9 months	3.20	765	13.7	525	7.8	350	0.2	0.4	4	0.3	0.4	50	25
10–12 months	3.61	865	14.9	525	7.8	350	0.3	0.4	5	0.4	0.4	50	25
1–3 years	4.86	1165	14.5	350	6.9	400	0.5	0.6	8	0.7	0.5	70	30
4–6 years	6.46	1545	19.7	450	6.1	500	0.7	0.8	11	0.9	0.8	100	30
7–10 years	7.28	1740	28.3	550	8.7	500	0.7	1.0	12	1.0	1.0	150	30
11–14 years	7.92	1845	41.2	800	14.8	600	0.7	1.1	12	1.0	1.2	200	35
15–18 years	8.83	2110	45.4	800	14.8	600	0.8	1.1	14	1.2	1.5	200	40
Women													
19–50 years	8.10	1940	45.0	700	14.8	600	0.8	1.1	13	1.2	1.5	200	40
pregnant	8.90	2140	51.0	700	14.8	700	0.9	1.4	13	1.2	1.5	300	50
lactating 1–3 months	10.30	2460	56.0	1250	14.8	950	1.0	1.6	15	1.2	2.0	260	70
lactating 4+ months	10.50	2470	53.0	1250	14.8	950	1.0	1.6	15	1.2	2.0	260	70
51–59 years	8.00	1900	46.5	700	8.7	600	0.8	1.1	13	1.2	1.5	200	40
60–64 years	7.99	1900	46.5	700	8.7	600	0.8	1.1	12	1.2	1.5	200	40
65–74 years	7.96	1900	46.5	700	8.7	600	0.8	1.1	12	1.2	1.5	200	40
over 75 years	7.61	1810	46.5	700	8.7	600	0.8	1.1	12	1.2	1.5	200	40

Table 12 Height/weight/age table for boys of school age (imperial)

| age | height (inches) | | | weight (lb) | | |
---	lower	average	upper	lower	average	upper
6	42	45	48	37	45	53
7	45	47	50	42	50	60
8	47	50	53	47	55	67
9	49	52	55	51	60	73
10	51	54	57	55	65	82
11	53	56	59	62	73	90
12	55	58	61	68	82	102
13	57	60	63	71	90	112
14	60	63	67	88	108	133
15	63	66	70	105	126	152
16	65	68	71	112	133	160
17	65	69	72	118	137	165

Height/weight/age table for boys of school age (metric)

| age | height (cm) | | | weight (kg) | | |
---	lower	average	upper	lower	average	upper
6	108	115	122	17	20	24
7	113	120	128	19	22	27
8	119	127	134	21	25	30
9	124	132	139	23	27	33
10	129	137	145	25	30	37
11	134	142	150	28	33	41
12	139	147	155	30	37	46
13	144	152	160	32	40	51
14	152	161	170	40	49	60
15	160	169	178	47	57	68
16	164	173	181	51	60	72
17	166	175	183	53	62	74

Table 13   Height/weight/age table for girls of school age (imperial)

age	height (inches)			weight (lb)		
	lower	average	upper	lower	average	upper
6	42	44	47	37	44	53
7	44	47	50	42	50	60
8	46	49	52	44	53	64
9	48	51	54	46	56	68
10	50	53	56	53	64	79
11	52	55	58	62	73	90
12	55	58	61	68	84	105
13	57	60	64	75	93	117
14	60	62	66	88	108	132
15	61	65	68	100	123	148
16	61	65	68	108	128	154
17	61	65	68	110	130	157

Height/weight/age table for girls of school age (metric)

age	height (cm)			weight (kg)		
	lower	average	upper	lower	average	upper
6	112	119	127	17	20	24
7	113	120	128	19	22	27
8	117	125	132	20	24	29
9	122	130	137	21	26	31
10	127	135	143	24	29	36
11	132	140	148	28	33	41
12	140	148	156	31	38	47
13	146	154	162	34	42	53
14	150	158	167	40	49	60
15	155	164	173	46	56	67
16	155	164	173	49	58	70
17	155	164	173	50	59	71

Table 14 Desirable weights for adults

Men					**Women**				
height *ft ' in "*	*weight in lb* lower	average	upper	obese	*height* *ft ' in "*	*weight in lb* lower	average	upper	obese
5' 2"	112	123	141	169	4' 10"	92	102	119	143
5' 3"	115	127	144	173	4' 11"	94	104	122	146
5' 4"	118	130	148	178	5' 0"	96	107	125	150
5' 5"	121	133	152	182	5' 1"	99	110	128	152
5' 6"	124	136	156	187	5' 2"	102	113	131	154
5' 7"	128	140	161	193	5' 3"	105	116	134	161
5' 8"	132	145	166	199	5' 4"	108	120	138	166
5' 9"	136	149	170	204	5' 5"	111	123	142	170
5' 10"	140	153	174	209	5' 6"	114	128	146	175
5' 11"	144	158	179	215	5' 7"	118	132	150	180
6' 0"	148	162	184	221	5' 8"	122	136	154	185
6' 1"	152	166	189	227	5' 9"	126	140	158	190
6' 2"	156	171	194	233	5' 10"	130	144	163	196
6' 3"	160	176	199	239	5' 11"	134	148	168	202
6' 4"	164	181	204	245	6' 0"	138	152	173	208

Men

height m	weight in kg lower	average	upper	obese
1.58	51	55.8	64	77
1.60	52	57.6	65	78
1.62	53	58.6	66	79
1.64	54	59.6	67	80
1.66	55	60.6	69	83
1.68	56	61.7	71	85
1.70	58	63.5	73	88
1.72	59	65.1	74	89
1.74	60	66.5	75	90
1.76	62	68.0	77	92
1.78	64	69.4	79	95
1.80	65	71.0	80	96
1.82	66	72.6	82	98
1.84	67	74.2	84	101
1.86	69	75.8	86	103
1.88	71	77.6	88	106
1.90	73	79.3	90	108
1.92	75	81	93	112

Women

height m	weight in kg lower	average	upper	obese
1.46	42	46.0	53	64
1.48	42	46.5	54	65
1.50	43	47.0	55	66
1.52	44	48.5	57	68
1.54	44	49.5	58	70
1.56	45	50.4	58	70
1.58	46	51.3	59	71
1.60	48	52.6	61	73
1.62	49	54.0	62	74
1.64	50	55.4	64	77
1.66	51	56.8	65	78
1.68	52	58.1	66	79
1.70	53	60.0	67	80
1.72	55	61.3	69	83
1.74	56	62.6	70	84
1.76	58	64.0	72	86
1.78	59	65.3	74	89

Eating out and prepared dishes

When you eat meals you have prepared at home, you can weigh the separate ingredients. You can then give a reasonably precise estimate of the nutrients, by adding up what each ingredient provides. When you eat out, this is not possible; everyone has a different recipe for each dish. You can only guess what has been included from experience.

Table 19 includes some values for made-up dishes, based on 'standard' or 'typical' recipes. These figures will provide a rough approximation, but often this is the only practical procedure.

The 'fast food' restaurants serve standard portions of foods prepared to standardized recipes; a hamburger from a fast food chain will be the same in every town. Therefore, within the usual limits discussed above, the nutrients in a standard meal from a fast food restaurant can be provided with reasonable accuracy.

Table 15 has been compiled from information provided by restaurants. Where information is not available, this is shown by 'na'.

Table 15   Energy yield, fat, sodium, and fibre content of the meals served in 'fast food' restaurants

Per standard portion	energy (kcal)	energy (kJ)	fat (g)	sodium (mg)	fibre (g)
Burger King					
Whopper Jr sandwich	370	1550	20	560	na
Whopper Jr with cheese	420	1760	25	780	na
Hamburger	290	1220	13	525	na
Regular French fries	210	880	11	230	na
Regular onion rings	270	1130	16	450	na
Apple pie	240	1010	12	335	na
Chocolate shake	340	1430	10	280	na
Homogenized milk	150	630	9	110	na
Kentucky Fried Chicken					
Chicken, one piece	220	920	14	na	na
Spare ribs	380	1600	24.5	na	0.4
Chips (small, 150 g)	340	1430	14.7	na	na
Jacket potato (200 g)	150	630	0.8	na	na
Coleslaw (small, 100 g)	120	500	8.2	na	0.9
Chicken sandwich	390	1640	16	na	na

Per standard portion	energy (kcal)	energy (kJ)	fat (g)	sodium (mg)	fibre (g)
Kentucky Fried Chicken *(continued)*					
Chicken, 2 pieces, and chips	780	3280	43	na	na
Colonel's Dinner	860	3610	44	na	na
Little Chef					
Prawn cocktail, bread, and butter	280	1180	17	na	na
Chef's grill	1030	4330	67	na	na
Fillet of cod	1000	4200	61	na	na
Gammon with fruit	370	1550	4.5	na	na
Cottage cheese with fruit	350	1470	3	na	na
Coleslaw (3 oz)	125	530	9	na	na
McDonald's					
Hamburger	260	1090	9.8	400	na
Quarter pounder	420	1760	21	720	na
Cheeseburger	300	1260	14	580	na
Big Mac	540	2270	28	1000	na
Egg McMuffin	330	1390	15	880	na
Hotcakes with butter and syrup	500	2100	10	1000	na
Apple pie	260	1090	15	145	na
Vanilla shake	350	1470	8	200	0
Fillet-o-Fish	420	1760	26	620	na
Regular Fries	290	1220	16	290	na
Pizzaland					
Cheese and tomato, traditional	700	2940	9	na	na
Special traditional	780	3280	8.6	na	na
Deep pan cheese and tomato	1160	4870	6.3	na	na
Deep pan special	1250	5250	7.4	na	na
Wendy					
Hamburger, single	470	1970	26	770	na
Hamburger, double	670	2810	40	980	na

Table 15 *continued*

Per standard portion	energy (kcal)	energy (kJ)	fat (g)	sodium (mg)	fibre (g)
Wendy *(continued)*					
Hamburger, triple	850	3570	51	1200	na
Cheese hamburger, single	580	2440	34	1100	na
Chili	230	970	8	1000	na
French fries	330	1390	16	110	na
Frosty	390	1640	16	250	na
Wimpy					
Hamburger	240	1010	9.4	600	1.8
Cheeseburger	280	1180	13	800	1.8
Kingsize hamburger	390	1640	21	1000	2.5
Quarter pounder	400	2100	28	1100	7
Fish and chips	490	2060	23	240	3.2
Chicken in a bun	430	1810	18	280	2.7
Chips (100 g, 3.5 oz)	290	1220	14	30	3.2
Apple pie	310	1300	13	240	2.4
Wimpy grill	520	2180	33	760	3.2
Thick shake	225	945	6.5	na	0
Fish and chip shops (typical figures)					
Chips (6 oz portion)	400	1680	18	0	4.2
Cod fried in batter (6 oz)	350	1470	17	170	0
Cod roe, fried	200	840	10	120	0

Table 16 Energy content of sauces and condiments

	quantity	kcal	kJ		quantity	kcal	kJ
Apple sauce	1 oz (30 g)	10	40	Mustard, prepared	1 tablespoon	10	40
Barbecue sauce	3 tablespoons	40	170	Piccalilli	2 tablespoons	40	170
Bread sauce	2 tablespoons	100	420	Pickled walnuts	1 oz (30 g)	150	630
Chocolate syrup or spread	2 tablespoons	120	500	Relish	1 tablespoon	30	130
Chutney (apple)	1 tablespoon	50	210	Sandwich spread	1 tablespoon	30	130
Cranberry sauce, sweetened	1 oz (30 g)	40	170	Seafood cocktail sauce	1 tablespoon	15	60
Cranberry jelly	1 oz (30 g)	70	290	Sesame seed	1 tablespoon	80	330
Croutons	1 oz (30 g)	120	500	Soy sauce	1 tablespoon	10	40
Custard	3 tablespoons	50	210	Sweet pickle	1 tablespoon	20	80
Gravy	4 fl oz (120 ml)	100	420	Tartar sauce	1 tablespoon	35	150
Hollandaise sauce	2 tablespoons	140	590	Teriyaki sauce	1 tablespoon	20	80
Horseradish sauce	2 tablespoons	60	250	Thousand Islands dressing	1 tablespoon	60	250
Italian garlic dressing	1 tablespoon	70	290	Tomato ketchup	1 tablespoon	15	60
Jams and preserves	2 tablespoons	80	330	Topping, whipped	3 tablespoons	100	420
Mint sauce	1 oz (30 g)	30	130	Wheat germ	1 tablespoon	50	210

Dietary fibre

Dietary fibre includes cellulose, insoluble non-cellulose polysaccharides and lignin (which together constitute *insoluble fibre*) and soluble non-cellulose polysaccharides (*soluble fibre*). It is derived from the cell walls of plant foods, and is not digested. It is important in the diet to provide bulk in the intestines.

The main sources of fibre are given in Table 17, using the same numbers for each food as in Table 19. Fibre content is not changed on cooking, apart from a gain or loss of water by the food. Difficulties in chemical analysis may result in slightly different values being found in some food composition tables.

Table 17 Dietary fibre content of foods (grams of dietary fibre / 100 g of food)

1 All-bran	30		**54** Beetroot, raw	3
2 Almonds	14		**58** Biscuits, chocolate	2
3 Apples	2		**59** Biscuits, cream crackers	6
Apricots, canned	1		**60** Biscuits, digestive	5
4 Apricots, fresh or stewed	2		**66** Blackberries	7
5 Apricots, dried, raw	24		**67** Blackcurrants	9
Apricots, dried, stewed	9		**·72** Bran, wheat	40
8 Asparagus	1		**73** Brazil nuts	9
9 Aubergine	2		**74** Bread, brown	7
10 Avocados	2		Bread, burger buns	4
19 Bananas	3		Bread, granary	7
20 Barcelona nuts	10		Bread, Hovis	5
21 Barley, pearl, raw	6		**75** Bread, malt	7
22 Barley, pearl, boiled	2		Bread, Vitbe	6
25 Beans, broad, boiled	4		**76** Bread, white	4
26 Beans, butter, raw	22		**78** Bread, wholemeal	7.5
27 Beans, butter, boiled	5		**82** Broccoli	4
28 Beans, French	3		**84** Brussels sprouts, raw	4
29 Beans, haricot, raw	25		**85** Brussels sprouts, boiled	3
30 Beans, haricot, boiled	7		**88** Cabbage, raw	3
Beansprouts, canned	3		**89** Cabbage, boiled	2

Table 17 *continued*   *(grams of fibre / 100 g of food)*

94	Cake, fruit	3	**184**	Flour, white	3
97	Cakes, sponge	1	**186**	Flour, wholemeal	9
99	Cakes, fancy	2	**193**	Gooseberries	3
100	Carrots	3	**194**	Grapenuts	6
102	Cauliflower	2	**195**	Grapefruit	0.5
106	Celery	2	**197**	Grapes	0.5
108	Chapatis, made with fat	7		Laverbread	3
109	Chapatis, made without fat	6	**235**	Leeks	3
	Chapati flour, fine	4	**244**	Lentils, raw	12
	Chapati flour, brown	10	**245**	Lentils, boiled	4
119	Cherries	2	**246**	Lettuce	1.5
121	Chestnuts	7	**252**	Loganberries	6
130	Christmas pudding	3		Lychees	0.5
135	Coconut, fresh	14		Mandarin oranges, canned	0.5
136	Coconut, desiccated	24	**263**	Marrow, raw	2
144	Cornflakes	11	**264**	Marrow, boiled	1
149	Cranberries	4	**267**	Matzo	4
154	Crispbread, rye	12	**269**	Melons	1
155	Crispbread, wheat, starch reduced	5	**282**	Muesli	8
156	Cucumber	0.5	**283**	Mushrooms	3
157	Currants, dry	7	**288**	Nectarines	2
161	Dates, dried	9	**289**	Oatmeal, raw	7
168	Dumplings	1	**292**	Okra	3
176	Endive	2	**295**	Onions, raw or boiled	1
178	Figs, dried, raw	19	**297**	Onions, fried	5
	Figs, dried, stewed	10	**298**	Onions, spring	3
	Figs, fresh	3	**299**	Oranges	2
183	Flour, brown	7	**302**	Pancakes	1
	Flour, rye	6	**304**	Parsnip, raw	4

Table 17 *continued* *(grams of fibre / 100 g of food)*

305	Parsnip, boiled	2.5	**390**	Scones	2
306	Pastry, flaky	2	**394**	Shredded Wheat	10
307	Pastry, shortcrust	2.5		Shreddies	11
308	Peaches, fresh	1	**402**	Soya flour, full fat	11
309	Peaches, canned	1		Soya, textured, dry	13
	Peaches, dried, raw	14		Soya, textured, cooked	3
	Peaches, dried, cooked	5	**404**	Spaghetti, raw	5
311	Peanuts	8		Spaghetti, brown, raw	12
313	Pears	2	**405**	Spaghetti, cooked	2
314	Peas	5		Spaghetti, brown, cooked	4
321	Chickpeas, raw	15	**406**	Spaghetti, canned in tomato sauce	3
322	Chickpeas, cooked	6	**407**	Special K	3
323	Peppers (green or red)	1	**408**	Spinach, boiled	6
	Pigeon peas, raw	15	**412**	Spring greens, boiled	4
326	Pineapple, fresh or canned	1	**414**	Strawberries	2
332	Plantain	6	**418**	Sugar Puffs	5
336	Plums	2	**419**	Sultanas, dry	7
344	Potatoes	2	**420**	Swedes	3
346	Potato crisps	12	**422**	Sweet potatoes	2
348	Prunes, dried, raw	16	**427**	Sweetcorn	4
349	Prunes, dried, stewed	8	**429**	Tangerines	2
350	Puffed Wheat	9	**434**	Tomatoes, raw	1.5
354	Radishes	1	**436**	Tomatoes, fried	3
355	Raisins, dry	7	**448**	Turnips	2
356	Raspberries	8	**455**	Walnuts	5
357	Ready Brek	7	**456**	Watercress	3
358	Red currants	7	**458**	Weetabix	12
359	Rhubarb	2	**459**	White currants	7
361	Rice Krispies	1	**466**	Yam	4
363	Rice, white, raw	3	**470**	Yorkshire pudding	1

Vitamin D

Table 18 Vitamin D content of foods

		µg/100 g				µg/100 g
63	Biscuits, shortbread	0.2			Liver, lamb	0.5
87	*Butter	0.8			Liver, ox	1.1
94	Cake, fruit	1.1			Liver, pig	1.1
97	Cake, sponge, with fat	2.8			Liver, calf	0.3
98	Cake, sponge, without fat	1.0		**256**	Macaroni cheese	0.3
110	Cheese, Camembert type, soft	0.2		**257**	Mackerel	17.5
111	Cheese, Cheddar type, hard	0.3		**260**	Margarine	8.0
113	Cheese, cream	0.3		**271**	*Milk, whole, fresh	0.03
114	Cheese, Danish Blue	0.2		**273**	*Milk, whole, Channel Islands	0.04
115	Cheese, Edam type	0.2		**275**	*Milk, whole, condensed	0.09
116	Cheese, Parmesan	0.3		**277**	*Milk, whole, dried	0.2
117	Cheese, processed	0.2		**279**	*Milk, goats'	0.06
118	Cheese, Stilton	0.3		**280**	Milk, human	0.03
130	Christmas pudding	0.2		**302**	Pancakes	0.2
150	*Cream, double	0.4			Pancakes, Scotch	1.3
151	*Cream, single	0.2		**306**	Pastry, flaky, cooked	1.8
152	*Cream, sterilised, canned	0.1		**307**	Pastry, shortcrust, cooked	1.4
153	*Cream, whipping	0.3		**325**	Pilchards, canned in tomato	8.0
158	Custard, egg	0.4		**352**	Quiche Lorraine	1.0
	Eclairs	0.9			Rock cakes	1.5
171	Eggs, whole	1.8		**365**	Roe, cod, hard	2.0
173	Egg yolk	5.0				
	Gingerbread	1.2				
194	Grapenuts	3.5				
210	Herring	22.5				
	Liver, chicken	0.2				

* The vitamin D content of milk depends on the season, being highest in summer, and lowest in winter. The figures quoted here are the summer averages for milk and milk products; winter levels are about half this.

Composition of foods

Table 19   Energy, protein, mineral, and vitamin contents of foods per 100 g

	Energy (kcal)	Energy (kJ)	Protein (g)	Fat (g)	Carb (g)	Water (g)	Sodium (mg)	Calcium (mg)	Iron (mg)	Vit A (μg)	Vit B$_1$ (mg)	Vit B$_2$ (mg)	Niacin (mg)	Vit C (mg)
1 All-Bran breakfast cereal	250	1040	13.0	2.5	46.0	5.0	1700	85	9.0	0	1.00	1.50	16.0	0
2 Almonds	560	2340	17.0	54.0	4.0	5.0	0	250	4.0	0	0.20	1.00	2.0	0
3 Apples	35	150	0.2	0	9.0	65.0	0	0	0.2	0	0.03	0	0.1	2
4 Apricots	30	120	0.6	0	7.0	87.0	0	0	0.4	250	0.04	0.05	0.6	10
5 Apricots, dried, raw	180	750	4.0	0	43.0	15.0	60	90	2.5	580	0	0.20	4.0	0
6 Artichokes, globe, boiled	15	60	1.0	0	3.0	84.0	0	0	0.5	0	0.03	0	1.0	10
7 Artichokes, Jerusalem, boiled	20	80	1.5	0	3.0	80.0	0	30	0.4	0	0.10	0	0	2
8 Asparagus, boiled	10	40	1.7	0	0.5	46.0	0	0	0.5	50	0.05	0.04	0.4	10
9 Aubergine, raw	15	60	0.7	0	3.0	93.0	0	0	0.4	0	0.05	0.03	0.8	5
10 Avocados	220	920	4.0	20.0	2.0	70.0	0	15	1.5	15	0.10	0.10	1.0	15
11 Bacon, collar joint, raw	320	1340	15.0	29.0	0	51.0	1700	0	1.2	0	0.40	0.20	3.0	0
12 Bacon, collar joint, boiled	330	1380	20.0	27.0	0	49.0	1100	0	1.5	0	0.30	0.20	2.5	0
13 Bacon, gammon rashers, grilled	230	960	30.0	12.0	0	52.0	2000	0	1.4	0	0.90	0.25	6.3	0
14 Bacon, gammon joint, raw	240	1000	18.0	18.0	0	60.0	1200	0	1.0	0	0.60	0.20	4.0	0
15 Bacon, gammon joint, boiled	270	1130	25.0	19.0	0	53.0	1000	0	1.3	0	0.40	0.15	3.5	0
16 Bacon rashers, streaky, raw	400	1670	15.0	40.0	0	41.0	1500	0	1.0	0	0.40	0.15	3.2	0
17 Bacon rashers, streaky, fried	500	2090	23.0	45.0	0	27.0	1800	0	1.2	0	0.40	0.20	4.5	0
18 Bacon rashers, streaky, grilled	400	1670	25.0	36.0	0	34.0	2000	0	1.5	0	0.40	0.16	4.2	0
19 Bananas	80	330	1.0	0.3	20.0	70.0	0	0	0.4	200	0.04	0.07	0.6	10
20 Barcelona nuts	640	2680	11.0	64.0	5.0	5.0	0	170	3.0	0	0.10	0.10	1.0	0
21 Barley, pearl, raw	360	1510	8.0	1.7	83.0	10.5	0	10	0.7	0	0.10	0.05	2.5	0
22 Barley, pearl, boiled	120	500	2.7	0.5	28.0	70.0	0	0	0.2	0	0	0	1.0	0
23 Bean sprouts, canned	10	40	1.6	0	0.8	95.0	80	0	1.0	0	0	0.03	0.2	0
24 Beans, baked, canned in tomato sauce	65	270	5.0	0.5	10.0	74.0	480	45	1.4	0	0.07	0.05	0.5	0

28

per 100 g	Energy (kcal)	Energy (kJ)	Protein (g)	Fat (g)	Carb (g)	Water (g)	Sodium (mg)	Calcium (mg)	Iron (mg)	Vit A (µg)	Vit B₁ (mg)	Vit B₂ (mg)	Niacin (mg)	Vit C (mg)
25 Beans, broad, boiled	50	210	4.0	0.6	7.0	84.0	20	20	1.0	40	0.10	0.04	3.0	15
26 Beans, butter, raw	270	1130	19.0	1.0	50.0	12.0	60	85	5.9	0	0.50	0.10	2.5	0
27 Beans, butter, boiled	100	420	7.0	0.3	17.0	71.0	0	20	1.7	0	0.10	0	0.3	0
28 Beans, French, boiled	7	30	0.8	0	1.0	96.0	0	40	0.6	80	0.04	0.07	0.3	5
29 Beans, haricot, raw	270	1130	21.0	1.5	46.0	11.0	45	80	6.7	0	0.45	0.13	2.5	0
30 Beans, haricot, boiled	90	380	6.6	0.5	17.0	70.0	0	70	2.5	0	0.20	0.05	0.3	0
31 Beans, mung, green, raw	230	960	22.0	1.0	36.0	12.0	30	100	8.0	0	0.45	0.20	2.0	0
32 Beans, mung, cooked (dahl) see also Lentils, number 245	100	420	6.0	4.0	11.0	73.0	820	35	2.6	0	0.10	0.04	0.4	0
33 Beans, red kidney, raw	270	1130	22.0	1.7	45.0	11.0	40	140	6.7	0	0.50	0.20	2.0	0
34 Beans, runner, raw	25	100	2.3	0.2	4.0	89.0	0	30	0.8	70	0.05	0.10	0.9	20
35 Beans, runner, boiled	20	85	2.0	0.2	3.0	91.0	0	25	0.7	60	0.03	0.07	0.5	5
36 Beef, brisket, raw	250	1050	17.0	20.0	0	62.0	70	0	1.5	0	0.05	0.15	4.0	0
37 Beef, brisket, boiled	320	1340	27.0	24.0	0	48.0	70	0	2.8	0	0.04	0.30	4.3	0
38 Beef, corned (canned)	220	920	27.0	12.0	0	59.0	1000	0	3.0	0	0	0.20	2.5	0
39 Beef, minced, raw	220	920	19.0	16.0	0	64.0	90	0	2.7	0	0.06	0.30	4.0	0
40 Beef, minced, stewed	230	960	23.0	15.0	0	59.0	300	0	3.1	0	0.05	0.33	4.4	0
41 Beef, rump steak, raw	200	840	19.0	14.0	0	67.0	50	0	2.3	0	0.08	0.26	4.2	0
42 Beef, rump steak, fried	250	1050	29.0	15.0	0	56.0	50	0	3.2	0	0.08	0.35	5.5	0
43 Beef, rump steak, grilled	220	920	27.0	12.0	0	59.0	50	0	3.4	0	0.08	0.30	6.0	0
44 Beef, silverside, salted	240	1000	29.0	14.0	0	54.0	900	0	2.8	0	0.03	0.30	3.3	0
45 Beef, sirloin, raw	270	1130	17.0	23.0	0	59.0	50	0	1.6	0	0.04	0.20	4.2	0
46 Beef, sirloin, roast	280	1170	24.0	21.0	0	54.0	50	0	2.0	0	0.06	0.25	4.8	0
47 Beef steak, stewing, raw	180	750	20.0	10.0	0	69.0	70	0	2.1	0	0.06	0.23	4.2	0
48 Beef steak, stewing, stewed	220	920	30.0	11.0	0	57.0	350	0	3.0	0	0.03	0.33	3.6	0
49 Beef, topside, raw	180	750	20.0	11.0	0	68.0	40	0	1.9	0	0.05	0.21	4.8	0
50 Beef, topside, roast see also Sausages, numbers 381–383	200	840	27.0	12.0	0	60.0	50	0	2.6	0	0.07	0.31	5.7	0
51 Beer, bitter	30	130	0	0	2.0	—	0	0	0	0	0	0	0.3	0
52 Beer, lager	30	130	0	0	1.5	—	0	0	0	0	0	0	0.3	0

per 100 g	Energy (kcal)	Energy (kJ)	Protein (g)	Fat (g)	Carb (g)	Water (g)	Sodium (mg)	Calcium (mg)	Iron (mg)	Vit A (μg)	Vit B₁ (mg)	Vit B₂ (mg)	Niacin (mg)	Vit C (mg)
53 Beer, stout	40	170	0	0	4.0	—	25	0	0	0	0	0	0.3	0
54 Beetroot, raw	30	120	1.3	0	6.0	87.0	85	25	0.4	0	0.03	0.05	0	5
55 Beetroot, boiled	45	190	1.8	0	10.0	83.0	65	30	0.4	0	0	0.04	0	5
56 Bemax	350	1470	26.5	8.0	45.0	6.0	0	20	10.0	0	1.50	0.60	6.0	0
57 Bilberries	60	250	0.5	0	14.0	85.0	0	0	0.7	15	0	0	0.4	20
58 Biscuits, chocolate coated	520	2180	6.0	27.0	67.0	2.0	160	110	1.7	0	0.03	0.15	0.5	0
59 Biscuits, cream crackers	440	1840	9.5	16.0	68.0	4.0	600	100	1.7	0	0.15	0.10	1.5	0
60 Biscuits, digestive, plain	470	1970	10.0	20.0	66.0	4.5	440	110	2.0	0	0.15	0.10	1.5	0
61 Biscuits, digestive, chocolate coated	490	2050	7.0	24.0	66.0	2.5	450	85	2.0	0	0.10	0.10	1.5	0
62 Biscuits, semi-sweet	460	1930	7.0	17.0	75.0	2.5	400	120	2.0	0	0.15	0.10	1.5	0
63 Biscuits, shortbread	500	2090	6.0	26.0	65.5	5.0	270	100	1.5	250	0.15	0	1.0	0
64 Biscuits, wafers, filled	540	2260	5.0	30.0	66.0	2.0	70	70	1.6	0	0.10	0.10	0.5	0
65 Biscuits, water	440	1840	11.0	12.5	76.0	4.5	470	120	1.6	0	0.10	0.03	1.0	0
66 Blackberries	30	120	1.5	0	6.0	80.0	0	60	1.0	15	0.03	0.04	0.4	20
67 Black currants	30	120	1.0	0	7.0	77.0	0	60	1.5	30	0.03	0.06	0.3	200
68 Black pudding, fried	300	1260	13.0	22.0	15.0	44.0	1200	35	20.0	0	0.10	0.10	1.0	0
69 Bloater, grilled	250	1050	24.0	17.0	0	56.0	700	120	2.2	50	0	0.20	4.0	0
70 Bounty bar	470	1970	5.0	26.0	58.0	8.0	180	100	1.3	0	0.04	0.10	0.3	0
71 Brain, boiled	130	540	12.0	9.0	0	77.0	200	0	1.4	0	0.10	0.20	2.0	20
72 Bran, wheat	200	840	14.0	5.5	27.0	8.0	30	10	13.0	0	1.00	0.40	30.0	0
73 Brazil nuts	600	2510	12.0	60.0	4.0	5.0	0	180	2.8	0	1.00	0.12	1.6	0
74 Bread, brown	220	920	9.0	2.2	45.0	39.0	550	100	2.5	0	0.25	0.05	3.0	0
75 Bread, malt	250	1050	8.0	3.0	49.0	39.0	280	90	3.5	0	0	0	0	0
76 Bread, white	230	960	7.8	1.7	50.0	39.0	540	100	1.7	0	0.20	0.03	1.4	0
77 Bread, white toasted	300	1260	9.6	1.7	65.0	24.0	640	110	2.2	0	0.20	0.04	1.8	0
78 Bread, wholemeal	220	920	8.8	2.7	42.0	40.0	540	25	2.5	0	0.30	0.08	4.0	0
79 Bread rolls, starch reduced	380	1590	44.0	4.0	46.0	8.0	650	50	4.0	0	0	0	0	0
80 Bread rolls, white see also Crispbread, numbers 154 and 155 and Matzo, number 267	300	1260	10.0	7.0	54.0	29.0	600	120	1.8	0	0.25	0.10	1.5	0

per 100 g	Energy (kcal)	Energy (kJ)	Protein (g)	Fat (g)	Carb (g)	Water (g)	Sodium (mg)	Calcium (mg)	Iron (mg)	Vit A (µg)	Vit B₁ (mg)	Vit B₂ (mg)	Niacin (mg)	Vit C (mg)
81 Breadcrumbs, white	350	1470	12.0	2.0	77.0	10.0	750	130	3.0	0	0.20	0.04	2.0	0
82 Broccoli tops, raw	25	100	3.3	0	2.5	89.0	0	100	1.5	500	0.10	0.30	1.0	100
83 Broccoli tops, boiled	20	80	3.0	0	1.6	90.0	0	80	1.0	500	0.06	0.20	0.6	35
84 Brussels sprouts, raw	25	100	4.0	0	3.0	88.0	0	30	0.7	60	0.10	0.15	0.7	100
85 Brussels sprouts, boiled	20	80	3.0	0	1.7	92.0	0	25	0.5	60	0.06	0.10	0.4	40
86 Buns, currant	300	1260	7.0	8.0	55.0	29.0	100	90	2.5	0	0.20	0.03	1.5	0
87 Butter	750	3140	0.5	82.0	0	15.4	870	15	0.2	1000	0	0	0	0
88 Cabbage, savoy, raw	25	100	3.0	0	3.0	90.0	25	75	0.9	50	0.06	0.05	0.3	60
89 Cabbage, savoy, boiled	10	40	1.3	0	1.0	96.0	0	50	0.7	50	0.03	0.03	0	15
90 Cabbage, spring, boiled	7	30	1.0	0	1.0	97.0	0	30	0.5	100	0.03	0.03	0	25
91 Cabbage, white, raw	20	80	2.0	0	3.5	90.0	0	45	0.4	0	0.06	0.05	0.3	40
92 Cabbage, winter, raw	20	80	3.0	0	3.0	88.0	0	60	0.6	50	0.06	0.05	0.3	60
93 Cabbage, winter, boiled	15	60	1.7	0	2.3	93.0	0	40	0.4	50	0.03	0.03	0.2	20
94 Cake, fruit	330	1380	4.0	11.0	58.0	20.0	170	75	1.8	120	0.10	0.10	0.5	0
95 Cake, Madeira	400	1670	5.0	17.0	58.0	20.0	400	40	1.0	0	0.05	0.10	0.5	0
96 Cake, rock	400	1670	5.0	16.0	60.0	15.0	500	400	1.5	200	0	0.10	0	0
97 Cake, sponge, with fat	460	1920	6.5	27.0	53.0	15.0	350	140	1.4	300	0	0.10	0.5	0
98 Cake, sponge, without fat	300	1260	10.0	7.0	54.0	30.0	80	70	2.0	100	0.10	0.25	0.5	0
99 Cakes, various, fancy, iced	400	1670	4.0	15.0	69.0	13.0	250	45	1.5	0	0	0.05	0	0
100 Carrots, raw	25	100	0.7	0	5.0	90.0	100	50	0.6	2000	0.06	0.05	0.6	5
101 Carrots, boiled	20	80	0.6	0	4.0	92.0	50	40	0.4	2000	0.05	0.04	0.4	4
102 Cauliflower, raw	15	60	2.0	0	1.5	93.0	0	0	0.5	5	0.10	0.10	0.6	60
103 Cauliflower, boiled	10	40	1.5	0	0.8	95.0	0	0	0.4	5	0.06	0.06	0.4	20
104 Cauliflower cheese	100	420	6.0	8.0	5.0	78.0	·250	160	0.4	100	0.06	0.15	0.4	5
105 Celeriac, boiled	15	60	1.5	0	2.0	90.0	30	50	0.8	0	0.04	0.04	0.5	4
106 Celery, raw	10	40	1.0	0	1.3	94.0	140	50	0.6	0	0.03	0.03	0.3	7
107 Celery, boiled	5	20	0.6	0	0.7	96.0	70	50	0.4	0	0	0	0	5
108 Chapatis, made with fat	340	1420	8.0	13.0	50.0	29.0	130	70	2.3	0	0.25	0.05	1.7	0

per 100 g	Energy (kcal)	Energy (kJ)	Protein (g)	Fat (g)	Carb (g)	Water (g)	Sodium (mg)	Calcium (mg)	Iron (mg)	Vit A (µg)	Vit B₁ (mg)	Vit B₂ (mg)	Niacin (mg)	Vit C (mg)
109 Chapatis, made without fat	200	840	7.0	1.0	44.0	46.0	120	60	2.0	0	0.23	0.04	1.5	0
110 Cheese, camembert, soft type	300	1260	23.0	23.0	0	48.0	1400	400	1.0	250	0.05	0.60	1.0	0
111 Cheese, cheddar, hard type	400	1670	26.0	34.0	0	37.0	600	800	0.4	400	0.04	0.50	0	0
112 Cheese, cottage	100	420	14.0	0.5	1.5	79.0	450	60	0.1	30	0	0.20	0	0
113 Cheese, cream	440	1840	3.0	47.0	0	45.0	300	100	0.1	450	0	0.15	0	0
114 Cheese, Danish blue	360	1510	23.0	29.0	0	40.0	1400	580	0.2	300	0.03	0.60	1.0	0
115 Cheese, Edam, semi-hard type	300	1260	24.0	23.0	0	44.0	1000	750	0.2	300	0.04	0.40	0	0
116 Cheese, Parmesan	400	1670	35.0	30.0	0	28.0	750	1200	0.4	400	0	0.50	0.3	0
117 Cheese, processed	300	1260	22.0	25.0	0	43.0	1400	700	0.5	250	0	0.30	0	0
118 Cheese, Stilton	460	1930	26.0	40.0	0	28.0	1200	350	0.5	450	0.07	0.30	0.2	0
119 Cherries	40	170	0.5	0	10.0	70.0	0	0	0.3	15	0.04	0.06	0.3	5
120 Cherries, glace	200	840	0	0	56.0	44.0	70	40	3.0	0	0	0	0	0
121 Chestnuts	170	710	2.0	2.7	37.0	50.0	0	50	1.0	0	0.20	0.20	0.2	0
122 Chicken, raw, boned	120	500	21.0	4.0	0	74.0	80	0	0.7	0	0.10	0.20	8.0	0
123 Chicken, raw (meat and skin)	230	960	18.0	18.0	0	64.0	70	0	0.7	0	0.10	0.10	6.0	0
124 Chicken, boiled, boned	180	750	29.0	7.0	0	63.0	80	0	1.2	0	0.06	0.20	7.0	0
125 Chicken, roast, boned	150	630	25.0	5.0	0	68.0	80	0	0.8	0	0.10	0.20	8.0	0
126 Chicken, roast, (meat and skin) see also Soup, number 397	220	920	23.0	14.0	0	62.0	70	0	0.8	0	0.10	0.20	7.0	0
127 Chicory	10	40	0.8	0	1.5	96.0	0	0	0.7	0	0.05	0.05	0.5	4
128 Chocolate, milk	530	2220	8.0	30.0	59.0	2.0	120	220	1.6	0	0.10	0.20	0	0
129 Chocolate, plain see also Drinking chocolate, number 163 and Cocoa powder, number 134	530	2220	5.0	29.0	65.0	1.0	0	40	2.5	0	0.10	0.10	0.4	0
130 Christmas pudding	300	1260	5.0	12.0	48.0	39.0	240	90	2.0	20	0.10	0.10	0.7	0
131 Cider, dry	35	150	0	0	3.0	—	0	0	0.5	0	0	0	0	0
132 Cider, sweet	40	170	0	0	4.0	—	0	0	0.5	0	0	0	0	0
133 Cockles, boiled	50	210	11.0	0.3	0	79.0	3500	130	26.0	0	0	0	0	0
134 Cocoa powder see also Drinking chocolate, number 163	300	1260	19.0	22.0	12.0	3.0	1000	130	10.0	0	0.20	0.06	1.7	0
135 Coconut	350	1470	3.0	36.0	4.0	42.0	0	0	2.0	0	0	0	0.3	0
136 Coconut, desiccated	600	2510	6.0	62.0	6.0	2.0	30	20	3.5	0	0.06	0.04	0.6	0

	per 100 g	Energy (kcal)	Energy (kJ)	Protein (g)	Fat (g)	Carb (g)	Water (g)	Sodium (mg)	Calcium (mg)	Iron (mg)	Vit A (µg)	Vit B₁ (mg)	Vit B₂ (mg)	Niacin (mg)	Vit C (mg)
137	Cod fillet, raw	80	330	17.0	0.7	0	82.0	80	20	0.3	0	0.10	0.10	1.7	0
138	Cod fillet, baked	100	420	21.0	1.2	0	77.0	340	25	0.4	0	0.10	0.10	1.7	0
139	Cod fillet, fried	170	710	21.0	8.0	4.0	65.0	180	110	1.2	0	0.10	0.10	2.0	0
140	Cod fillet, fried in batter	200	840	20.0	10.0	8.0	61.0	100	80	0.5	0	0.10	0.10	1.2	0
141	Cod fillet, grilled	100	420	21.0	1.3	0	78.0	90	0	0.4	0	0.10	0.10	2.0	0
142	Cod fillet, poached	90	380	21.0	1.0	0	78.0	110	30	0.3	0	0.10	0.10	2.0	0
143	Cod fillet, steamed	80	330	19.0	1.0	0	79.0	100	0	0.5	0	0.10	0.10	2.0	0
144	Cornflakes breakfast cereal (enriched)	350	1500	8.0	0.5	82.0	3.0	1200	0	7.0	0	1.00	1.50	16.0	0
145	Cornflour	350	1470	0.6	0.7	92.0	12.0	50	15	1.4	0	0	0	0	0
146	Cornish pastie (2/3 pastry, 1/3 filling)	330	1380	8.0	20.0	31.0	39.0	600	60	1.5	0	0.10	0.10	1.6	0
147	Crab, boiled	130	540	20.0	5.0	0	73.0	400	30	1.3	0	0.10	0.20	2.5	0
148	Crab, canned	80	330	18.0	1.0	0	79.0	550	120	2.8	0	0	0.10	1.1	0
149	Cranberries	15	60	0.5	0	4.0	87.0	0	15	1.0	0	0.03	0	0	10
150	Cream, double	450	1880	1.5	48.0	2.0	48.0	30	50	0.2	400	0	0.10	0	0
151	Cream, single	200	840	2.4	21.2	3.0	72.0	40	80	0.3	250	0.03	0.10	0	0
152	Cream, sterilised, canned	230	960	2.6	23.0	3.0	70.0	60	80	0.3	200	0	0.10	0	0
153	Cream, whipping	330	1380	1.9	35.0	2.5	61.5	30	60	0.3	300	0	0.10	0	0
154	Crispbread, rye	320	1340	9.5	2.0	71.0	6.0	220	50	4.0	0	0.30	0.15	1.0	0
155	Crispbread, wheat, starch reduced see also Matzo, number 267	390	1630	45.0	7.5	37.0	5.0	600	60	5.5	0	0.15	0.10	4.0	0
156	Cucumber	10	40	0.6	0	2.0	96.0	0	25	0.3	0	0.04	0.04	0	8
157	Currants, dried	240	1000	2.0	0	63.0	20.0	0	100	2.0	0	0.03	0.08	0.5	0
158	Custard, egg	120	500	6.0	6.0	11.0	77.0	80	130	0.5	60	0.05	0.30	0	0
159	Custard, made with powder	120	500	4.0	4.0	17.0	75.0	80	140	0	40	0.05	0.20	0	0
160	Damsons	35	150	0.4	0	9.0	70.0	0	20	0.4	0	0.09	0.03	0.3	0
161	Dates, dried	210	880	2.0	0	55.0	12.0	0	60	1.5	0	0.06	0.03	1.7	0
162	Dogfish, fried in batter	270	1130	17.0	19.0	8.0	54.0	300	40	1.1	0	0.10	0.10	5.5	0
163	Drinking chocolate (powder) see also Cocoa powder, number 134	370	1550	6.0	6.0	77.0	2.0	250	30	2.4	0	0.06	0.04	0.5	0
164	Dripping see also Lard, number 234 and Suet, number 415	900	3770	0	100.0	0	0	0	0	0	0	0	0	0	0

per 100 g	Energy (kcal)	Energy (kJ)	Protein (g)	Fat (g)	Carb (g)	Water (g)	Sodium (mg)	Calcium (mg)	Iron (mg)	Vit A (μg)	Vit B₁ (mg)	Vit B₂ (mg)	Niacin (mg)	Vit C (mg)
165 Duck, raw, boned	120	500	20.0	5.0	0	75.0	100	0	2.4	0	0.40	0.50	5.0	0
166 Duck, raw, (meat and skin)	430	1800	11.0	43.0	0	44.0	80	0	2.4	0	0.30	0.40	4.0	0
167 Duck, roast, (meat and skin)	190	800	25.0	10.0	0	64.0	100	0	2.7	0	0.30	0.50	5.0	0
168 Dumpling	200	840	3.0	12.0	25.0	60.0	400	160	1.0	0	0	0	0.6	0
169 Eel, raw	170	710	17.0	11.0	0	71.0	90	0	0.7	1500	0.20	0.35	3.5	0
170 Eel, stewed	200	840	21.0	13.0	0	61.0	85	0	0.9	2000	0.10	0.40	3.0	0
171 Egg, whole, raw	150	630	12.3	10.9	0	74.8	140	50	2.0	140	0.10	0.50	0	0
172 Eggwhite	35	150	9.0	0	0	88.3	190	0	0	0	0	0.40	0	0
173 Egg yolk	340	1420	16.1	30.5	0	51.0	50	130	6.0	400	0.30	0.50	0	0
174 Egg, dried, whole	560	2340	43.6	43.3	0	7.0	520	190	8.0	500	0.35	1.20	0	0
175 Egg, scrambled	250	1050	10.0	23.0	0	62.0	1000	60	2.0	150	0.10	0.30	0	0
176 Endive	12	50	2.0	0	1.0	94.0	0	45	2.8	400	0.06	0.10	0.4	10
177 Fat, cooking see also Oil, number 291, Lard, number 234, Suet, number 415 and Dripping, number 164	900	3770	0	100.0	0	0	0	0	0	0	0	0	0	0
178 Figs, dried, raw	210	880	4.0	0	53.0	17.0	90	300	4.0	0	0.10	0.08	1.7	0
179 Fish fingers, frozen	180	750	13.0	7.5	16.0	64.0	320	45	0.7	0	0.10	0.10	1.1	0
180 Fish fingers, fried	230	960	13.5	13.0	17.0	56.0	350	45	0.7	0	0.10	0.10	1.4	0
181 Fishcakes, frozen	110	460	11.0	0.8	17.0	70.0	500	0	2.0	0	0.06	0.25	4.8	0
182 Fish paste	170	710	15.0	10.0	4.0	67.0	600	300	9.0	0	0	0.20	4.0	0
183 Flour, brown	330	1380	13.0	2.0	69.0	14.0	0	150	4.0	0	0.40	0.05	4.0	0
184 Flour, white	340	1420	11.0	1.2	75.0	14.5	0	40	2.0	0	0.30	0.03	2.0	0
185 Flour, white, self-raising	340	1420	9.0	1.2	77.5	13.0	350	350	2.5	0	0.30	0	1.5	0
186 Flour, wholemeal	320	1340	13.0	2.0	66.0	14.0	0	35	4.0	0	0.50	0.10	6.0	0
187 Fruit gums	170	710	1.0	0	45.0	12.0	60	360	4.2	0	0	0	0	0
188 Fruit juice, unsweetened	30	130	0	0	8.0	90.0	0	0	0.3	0	0.04	0	0.2	25
189 Fruit juice, sweetened	40	170	0	0	10.0	87.0	0	0	0.3	0	0.04	0	0.2	25
190 Fruit pie, individual	370	1550	4.0	16.0	56.0	23.0	200	50	1.0	0	0.05	0	0.4	0
191 Fruit salad, canned	90	380	0.3	0	25.0	70.0	0	0	1.0	0	0	0	0.3	0
192 Goose, roast meat	320	1340	29.0	22.0	0	47.0	150	0	4.6	na	na	na	na	na

per 100 g	Energy (kcal)	Energy (kJ)	Protein (g)	Fat (g)	Carb (g)	Water (g)	Sodium (mg)	Calcium (mg)	Iron (mg)	Vit A (µg)	Vit B₁ (mg)	Vit B₂ (mg)	Niacin (mg)	Vit C (mg)
193 Gooseberries	20	80	1.0	0	3.0	90.0	0	30	0.3	30	0.04	0.03	0.3	40
194 Grape-nuts (breakfast cereal)	360	1510	11.0	3.0	76.0	4.0	660	40	5.0	1300	1.20	1.60	17.0	0
195 Grapefruit, peeled	20	80	0.5	0	5.0	90.0	0	0	0.3	0	0.05	0	0.2	40
196 Grapefruit, canned in syrup	60	250	0.5	0	16.0	82.0	0	0	0.7	0	0.04	0	0.2	30
197 Grapes, black	50	210	0.5	0	13.0	65.0	0	0	0.3	0	0.04	0	0.3	0
198 Grapes, white	60	250	0.6	0	15.0	75.0	0	20	0.3	0	0.04	0	0.3	0
199 Greengages	50	210	1.0	0	11.0	75.0	0	0	0.4	0	0.05	0.03	0.4	0
200 Haggis, boiled	300	1260	11.0	22.0	19.0	46.0	800	30	5.0	2000	0.20	0.40	1.5	0
201 Halibut, raw	90	380	18.0	2.5	0	78.0	85	0	0.5	0	0.10	0.10	5.0	0
202 Halibut, steamed	130	540	24.0	4.0	0	71.0	110	0	0.6	0	0.10	0.10	5.0	0
203 Ham	120	500	18.0	5.0	0	73.0	1200	0	1.2	0	0.50	0.30	4.0	0
204 Hamburgers, raw	270	1130	15.0	21.0	5.0	56.0	600	25	2.5	0	0.04	0.20	4.0	0
205 Hamburgers, fried	260	1090	20.0	17.0	7.0	53.0	900	35	3.1	0	0	0.20	4.0	0
206 Hare, stewed (with bones)	140	590	22.0	6.0	0	44.0	30	0	8.0	na	na	na	na	na
207 Heart, raw	100	420	19.0	4.0	0	76.0	100	0	5.0	0	0.50	1.00	6.0	5
208 Heart, roast	240	1000	26.0	15.0	0	57.0	150	0	8.0	0	0.50	1.50	9.0	0
209 Heart, stewed	180	750	31.0	6.0	0	62.0	180	0	8.0	0	0.20	1.10	4.7	0
210 Herring, raw	230	960	17.0	19.0	0	64.0	70	35	0.8	50	0	0.20	4.0	0
211 Herring, fried in oatmeal	230	960	23.0	15.0	1.5	59.0	100	40	1.0	40	0	0.20	3.5	0
212 Herring, grilled	200	840	20.0	13.0	0	66.0	170	35	1.0	50	0	0.20	4.0	0
213 Honey	290	1210	0	0	76.0	23.0	0	0	0.4	0	0	0	0.2	0
214 Ice cream, dairy	170	710	4.0	7.0	25.0	64.0	80	140	0.2	0	0.04	0.20	0	0
215 Ice cream, non-dairy	170	710	3.0	8.0	21.0	66.0	70	120	0.3	0	0.04	0.15	0	0
216 Jams	260	1090	0	0	69.0	30.0	0	0	1.5	0	0	0	0	10
217 Jelly, packet	260	1090	6.0	0	63.0	30.0	25	30	2.0	0	0	0	0	0
218 Kidney, raw	90	380	17.0	3.0	0	79.0	220	0	7.0	100	0.50	1.80	8.0	10
219 Kidney, fried	150	630	25.0	6.0	0	67.0	250	0	12.0	160	0.60	2.30	10.0	10
220 Kidney, stewed	170	710	26.0	8.0	0	64.0	400	0	8.0	250	0.30	2.00	5.0	10

per 100 g	Energy (kcal)	Energy (kJ)	Protein (g)	Fat (g)	Carb (g)	Water (g)	Sodium (mg)	Calcium (mg)	Iron (mg)	Vit A (µg)	Vit B₁ (mg)	Vit B₂ (mg)	Niacin (mg)	Vit C (mg)
221 Kipper, baked	200	840	26.0	11.0	0	59.0	1000	70	1.4	50	0	0.20	4.0	0
222 Lamb, breast, raw	380	1590	17.0	35.0	0	48.0	100	0	1.3	0	0.08	0.17	3.8	0
223 Lamb, breast, roast	400	1670	19.0	37.0	0	44.0	70	0	1.5	0	0.06	0.17	3.4	0
224 Lamb, chops, loin, raw	380	1590	15.0	35.0	0	50.0	60	0	1.2	0	0.10	0.15	4.0	0
225 Lamb, chops, loin, grilled	350	1470	24.0	29.0	0	46.0	70	0	1.9	0	0.10	0.20	5.0	0
226 Lamb cutlets, raw	400	1670	15.0	36.0	0	48.0	60	0	1.2	0	0.10	0.15	4.0	0
227 Lamb cutlets, grilled	370	1550	23.0	31.0	0	45.0	70	0	1.9	0	0.10	0.20	4.8	0
228 Lamb, leg, raw	240	1000	18.0	19.0	0	63.0	50	0	1.7	0	0.14	0.25	5.7	0
229 Lamb, leg, roast	270	1130	26.0	18.0	0	55.0	65	0	2.5	0	0.12	0.30	5.4	0
230 Lamb, scrag and neck, raw	300	1260	16.0	28.0	0	56.0	70	0	1.2	0	0.10	0.20	3.5	0
231 Lamb, scrag and neck, stewed	290	1210	26.0	21.0	0	53.0	240	0	2.2	0	0.04	0.20	2.7	0
232 Lamb, shoulder, raw	300	1260	16.0	28.0	0	56.0	70	0	1.2	0	0.10	0.20	3.6	0
233 Lamb, shoulder, roast	320	1340	20.0	26.0	0	54.0	60	0	1.6	0	0.10	0.20	3.6	0
234 Lard see also Dripping, number 164 and Suet, number 415	900	3770	0	100.0	0	0	0	0	0	0	0	0	0	0
235 Leeks, raw	30	125	2.0	0	6.0	86.0	0	65	1.1	0	0.10	0.05	0.6	20
236 Leeks, boiled	25	105	1.8	0	5.0	91.0	0	60	2.0	0	0.07	0.03	0.4	15
237 Lemons	15	60	1.0	0	3.0	85.0	0	100	0.4	0	0.05	0.04	0	80
238 Lemon juice	5	20	0.3	0	1.5	90.0	0	0	0	0	0	0	0	50
239 Lemonade, bottled	20	80	0	0	6.0	95.0	0	0	0	0	0	0	0	0
240 Lemon curd	280	1170	0	5.0	63.0	30.0	70	0	0.5	0	0	0	0	0
241 Lemon sole, raw	80	330	17.0	1.4	0	81.0	100	0	0.5	0	0.10	0.10	3.5	0
242 Lemon sole, fried in breadcrumbs	200	840	16.0	13.0	9.0	60.0	140	100	1.1	0	0.10	0.10	3.0	0
243 Lemon sole, steamed	90	380	21.0	1.0	0	77.0	120	25	0.6	0	0.10	0.10	3.6	0
244 Lentils, raw	300	1260	24.0	1.0	53.0	12.0	40	40	7.6	10	0.50	0.20	2.0	0
245 Lentils, boiled see also Beans, mung (dahl), number 32	100	420	8.0	0.5	17.0	72.0	0	0	2.4	0	0.10	0.04	0.4	0
246 Lettuce	10	40	1.0	0	1.0	96.0	0	25	0.9	200	0.07	0.08	0.3	15
247 Liquorice allsorts	310	1300	4.0	2.0	74.0	7.0	75	60	8.0	0	0	0	0	0

per 100 g	Energy (kcal)	Energy (kJ)	Protein (g)	Fat (g)	Carb (g)	Water (g)	Sodium (mg)	Calcium (mg)	Iron (mg)	Vit A (µg)	Vit B₁ (mg)	Vit B₂ (mg)	Niacin (mg)	Vit C (mg)
248 Liver, raw	150	630	20.0	7.0	2.0	70.0	90	0	8.0	1500	0.20	3.10	12.0	20
249 Liver, fried	250	1050	27.0	13.0	7.0	53.0	170	0	7.5	1700	0.30	4.20	16.0	10
250 Liver, stewed see also Sausage, liver sausage, number 380	200	840	25.0	10.0	3.0	63.0	110	0	8.0	2000	0.20	3.60	10.0	15
251 Lobster, boiled	120	500	22.0	3.5	0	72.0	330	60	0.8	0	0.10	0.10	1.5	0
252 Loganberries	20	80	1.0	0	3.5	85.0	0	40	1.5	0	0	0.03	0.4	40
253 Luncheon meat (canned)	300	1260	13.0	27.0	5.0	51.0	1000	15	1.0	0	0.07	0.10	2	0
254 Macaroni, raw	370	1550	14.0	2.0	79.0	10.0	30	30	1.5	0	0.10	0.06	2.0	0
255 Macaroni, boiled	120	500	4.0	0.6	25.0	71.0	0	0	0.5	0	0	0	0.3	0
256 Macaroni cheese	170	710	7.0	10.0	15.0	67.0	300	200	0.4	100	0.03	0.15	0	0
257 Mackerel, raw	220	920	19.0	16.0	0	64.0	130	25	1.0	45	0.10	0.35	8.0	0
258 Mackerel, fried	190	790	22.0	11.0	0	66.0	150	30	1.2	50	0.10	0.40	9.0	0
259 Mangoes, fresh	60	250	0.5	0	15.0	83.0	0	0	0.5	1000	0.03	0.04	0.3	30
260 Margarine	730	3060	0	81.0	0	16.0	800	0	0	1000	0	0	0	0
261 Margarine, low fat spread	370	1550	0	40.0	0	57.0	700	0	0	1000	0	0	0	0
262 Marmalade	260	1090	0	0	69.0	28.0	0	35	0.6	50	0	0	0	10
263 Marrow, raw	15	60	0.6	0	4.0	94.0	0	0	0.2	5	0	0	0.3	5
264 Marrow, boiled	7	30	0.4	0	1.4	98.0	0	0	0.2	5	0	0	0.2	2
265 Mars bar	440	1840	5.0	19.0	67.0	7.0	150	160	1.0	0	0.05	0.20	0.3	0
266 Marzipan	440	1840	9.0	25.0	49.0	10.0	0	120	2.0	0	0.10	0.50	0.9	0
267 Matzo	380	1590	10.5	2.0	87.0	7.0	20	30	1.5	0	0.10	0.03	1.0	0
268 Mayonnaise see also Salad cream, number 368	720	3010	2.0	79.0	0	28.0	360	0	0.7	80	0.06	0.10	0	0
269 Melons	25	100	0.5	0	5.0	93.0	0	0	0.5	1000	0.05	0.03	0.5	25
270 Meringues, made with egg white	380	1590	5.0	0	96.0	2.0	100	0	0.1	0	0	0.25	0.1	0
271 Milk	65	270	3.3	3.8	4.7	87.6	50	120	0	50	0.05	0.20	0.1	1
272 Milk, skimmed	33	140	3.4	0.1	5.0	90.9	50	130	0	0	0.04	0.20	0.1	1
273 Milk, Channel Islands	75	310	3.6	4.8	4.7	86.3	50	120	0	50	0.05	0.20	0.1	1
274 Milk, condensed, skimmed	270	1130	9.9	0.3	60.0	27.0	180	380	0.3	0	0.10	0.60	0.3	2

per 100 g	Energy (kcal)	Energy (kJ)	Protein (g)	Fat (g)	Carb (g)	Water (g)	Sodium (mg)	Calcium (mg)	Iron (mg)	Vit A (µg)	Vit B₁ (mg)	Vit B₂ (mg)	Niacin (mg)	Vit C (mg)
275 Milk, condensed, whole, sweetened	320	1340	8.3	9.0	55.5	25.8	130	280	0.2	100	0.10	0.50	0.2	2
276 Milk, dried, skimmed	355	1490	36.4	1.3	52.8	4.1	550	1200	0.4	0	0.40	1.60	1.2	6
277 Milk, dried, whole	490	2050	26.3	26.3	39.4	2.9	440	1000	0.4	350	0.30	1.00	0.6	10
278 Milk, evaporated, whole	160	670	8.6	9.0	11.3	68.6	180	280	0	100	0.06	0.50	0.3	0
279 Milk, goat	70	290	3.3	4.5	4.6	87.0	40	130	0	40	0.04	0.15	0	0
280 Milk, human	70	290	1.3	4.1	7.2	87.1	14	35	0.1	60	0.02	0.03	0.2	4
281 Mincemeat	240	1000	0	4.0	62.0	27.0	140	30	1.5	0	0	0	0	0
282 Muesli	370	1550	13.0	7.5	66.0	6.0	180	200	4.5	0	0.30	0.30	3.0	0
283 Mushrooms, raw	15	60	2.0	0.6	0	92.0	0	0	1.0	0	0.10	0.40	4.0	3
284 Mushrooms, fried see also Soup, number 398	210	880	2.2	22.0	0	64.0	0	0	1.3	0	0.07	0.40	3.5	0
285 Mussels, raw	70	290	12.0	2.0	0	84.0	300	100	6.0	0	0	0	0	0
286 Mussels, boiled	90	380	17.0	2.0	0	79.0	200	200	7.7	0	0	0	0	0
287 Mustard and cress	10	40	1.5	0	1.0	93.0	0	70	1.0	100	0	0	0	40
288 Nectarines	50	210	1.0	0	11.0	74.0	0	0	0.4	500	0	0.05	0.9	10
289 Oatmeal, raw	400	1670	12.0	9.0	73.0	9.0	30	60	4.1	0	0.50	0.10	1.0	0
290 Oatmeal porridge (10% wt)	45	190	1.5	1.0	8.0	90.0	600	0	0.5	0	0.05	0	0	0
291 Oil, vegetable see also Fat, number 177	900	3770	0	100.0	0	0	0	0	0	0	0	0	0	0
292 Okra, raw	20	80	2.0	0	2.0	90.0	0	70	1.0	15	0.10	0.10	1.0	25
293 Olives, pickled	80	330	1.0	9.0	0	60.0	1800	50	1.0	100	0	0	0	0
294 Omelette	200	840	11.0	16.0	0	69.0	1000	50	2.0	200	0.10	0.30	0	0
295 Onions, raw	25	100	1.0	0	5.0	93.0	0	30	0.3	0	0.03	0.05	0	10
296 Onions, boiled	10	40	0.6	0	3.0	97.0	0	25	0.3	0	0	0.04	0	5
297 Onions, fried	350	1470	2.0	33.0	10.0	42.0	0	60	0.6	0	0	0	0	0
298 Onions, spring	35	150	1.0	0	8.5	87.0	0	140	1.2	0	0.03	0.05	0.2	25
299 Oranges, peeled	35	150	1.0	0	9.0	85.0	0	40	0.3	50	0.10	0.03	0.2	50
300 Orange juice	40	170	0.6	0	9.0	87.0	0	0	0.3	50	0.08	0	0.2	50
301 Oxtail, stewed (with bones) see also Soup, number 199	90	380	12.0	5.0	0	21.0	70	0	1.4	0	0	0.10	1.3	0
302 Pancakes	300	1260	6.0	16.0	36.0	43.0	50	120	1.0	40	0.10	0.20	0.6	0

per 100 g	Energy (kcal)	Energy (kJ)	Protein (g)	Fat (g)	Carb (g)	Water (g)	Sodium (mg)	Calcium (mg)	Iron (mg)	Vit A (µg)	Vit B₁ (mg)	Vit B₂ (mg)	Niacin (mg)	Vit C (mg)
303 Parsley	20	80	5.0	0	0	79.0	35	330	8.0	1500	0.15	0.30	1.0	150
304 Parsnips, raw	50	210	2.0	0	11.0	83.0	0	60	0.6	0	0.10	0.08	1.0	15
305 Parsnips, boiled	60	250	1.3	0	13.5	83.0	0	40	0.5	0	0.07	0.06	0.7	10
306 Pastry, flaky, cooked	560	2340	6.0	40.0	47.0	7.0	500	90	1.5	200	0.10	0	1.0	0
307 Pastry, shortcrust, cooked	530	2220	7.0	32.0	56.0	7.0	500	100	2.0	150	0.20	0	1.3	0
308 Peaches, fresh	30	130	0.5	0	8.0	75.0	0	0	0.3	70	0	0.04	0.9	10
309 Peaches, canned in syrup	90	380	0.5	0	23.0	74.0	0	0	0.4	40	0	0	0.6	0
310 Peanut butter	620	2600	23.0	54.0	13.0	1.0	350	40	2.0	0	0.20	0.10	15.0	0
311 Peanuts, fresh	570	2390	24.0	50.0	9.0	4.0	0	60	2.0	0	1.00	0.10	16.0	0
312 Peanuts, roasted and salted	570	2390	24.0	50.0	9.0	4.0	450	60	2.0	0	0.20	0.10	16.0	0
313 Pears	30	130	0.2	0	8.0	60.0	0	0	0	0	0	0	0	0
314 Peas, fresh or frozen	70	290	6.0	0.4	11.0	78.0	0	0	2.0	50	0.30	0.20	2.5	25
315 Peas, boiled	50	210	5.0	0.4	8.0	80.0	0	0	1.2	50	0.30	0.15	2.5	25
316 Peas, canned	50	210	5.0	0.3	7.0	82.0	230	25	1.6	50	0.10	0.10	2.0	8
317 Peas, dried, raw	290	1210	22.0	1.3	50.0	13.0	40	60	4.7	50	0.60	0.30	3.0	0
318 Peas, dried, boiled	100	420	7.0	0.4	19.0	70.0	0	25	1.4	50	0.60	0.30	3.0	0
319 Peas, split, dried, raw	310	1300	22.0	1.0	57.0	12.0	40	35	5.4	30	0.70	0.20	3.2	0
320 Peas, split, dried, boiled	120	500	8.0	0.3	22.0	67.0	0	0	1.7	0	0.10	0.06	1.0	0
321 Peas, chickpeas, raw	320	1340	20.0	6.0	50.0	10.0	40	140	6.4	30	0.50	0.15	1.5	3
322 Peas, chickpeas, cooked	140	590	8.0	3.3	22.0	66.0	850	65	3.1	90	0.10	0.05	0.5	3
323 Peppers, green, raw	15	60	1.0	0.4	2.0	94.0	0	0	0.4	40	0	0.03	0.7	100
324 Peppers, green, boiled	15	60	1.0	0.4	2.0	94.0	0	0	0.4	40	0	0	0.6	60
325 Pilchards, canned in tomato sauce	130	540	19.0	5.0	0.7	70.0	400	300	2.7	0	0	0.30	8.0	0
326 Pineapple, fresh	50	210	0.5	0	12.0	84.0	0	0	0.4	0	0.08	0	0.2	25
327 Pineapple, canned in syrup	80	330	0.3	0	20.0	77.0	0	0	0.4	0	0.05	0	0.2	10
328 Plaice, raw	90	380	18.0	2.2	0	80.0	120	50	0.3	0	0.30	0.10	3.2	0
329 Plaice, fried in batter	280	1170	16.0	18.0	14.0	52.0	220	90	1.0	0	0.20	0.15	2.0	0
330 Plaice, fried in breadcrumbs	230	960	18.0	14.0	9.0	60.0	220	70	0.8	0	0.20	0.20	3.0	0

per 100 g	Energy (kcal)	Energy (kJ)	Protein (g)	Fat (g)	Carb (g)	Water (g)	Sodium (mg)	Calcium (mg)	Iron (mg)	Vit A (µg)	Vit B₁ (mg)	Vit B₂ (mg)	Niacin (mg)	Vit C (mg)
331 Plaice, steamed	90	380	19.0	2.0	0	78.0	120	40	0.6	0	0.30	0.10	3.2	0
332 Plantain, raw, green	110	460	1.0	0.2	28.0	67.0	0	0	0.5	0	0.05	0.05	0.7	20
333 Plantain, boiled	120	500	2.0	0	31.0	64.0	0	0	0.4	0	0	0	0.3	3
334 Plantain, ripe, fried	270	1130	1.5	9.0	48.0	35.0	0	0	0.8	20	0.10	0	0.6	12
335 Plums, cooking, raw	20	80	0.5	0	6.0	77.0	0	0	0.3	30	0.05	0.03	0.5	0
336 Plums, dessert	40	160	0.5	0	10.0	84.0	0	0	0.4	30	0.05	0.03	0.5	0
337 Pork pie (40% meat)	380	1590	10.0	27.0	25.0	37.0	700	50	1.4	0	0.20	0.10	1.8	0
338 Pork chops, loin, raw	330	1380	16.0	30.0	0	54.0	50	0	0.8	0	0.60	0.15	4.2	0
339 Pork chops, loin, grilled	330	1380	29.0	24.0	0	46.0	80	0	1.2	0	0.70	0.20	5.7	0
340 Pork, leg, raw	270	1130	17.0	23.0	0	59.0	60	0	0.8	0	0.70	0.20	4.5	0
341 Pork, leg, roast see also Sausages, numbers 385-387 Porridge, see Oatmeal, number 290	290	1210	27.0	20.0	0	52.0	80	0	1.3	0	0.70	0.30	5.0	0
342 Potatoes, raw	90	380	2.0	0	21.0	76.0	0	0	0.5	0	0.10	0.04	1.2	15
343 Potatoes, baked with skin	85	360	2.0	0	20.0	58.0	0	0	0.6	0	0.10	0.03	1.0	10
344 Potatoes, boiled	80	330	1.4	0	20.0	81.0	0	0	0.3	0	0.10	0.03	1.0	10
345 Potato chips see also Sweet potatoes, number 422	250	1050	4.0	11.0	37.0	47.0	0	0	0.9	0	0.10	0.04	1.2	10
346 Potato crisps	530	2200	6.0	35.0	50.0	3.0	600	40	2.0	0	0.20	0.10	5.0	15
347 Prawns, boiled	100	420	23.0	2.0	0	70.0	1600	150	1.1	0	0	0	0	0
348 Prunes, raw	130	540	2.0	0	34.0	20.0	0	30	2.5	130	0.08	0.20	1.0	0
349 Prunes, stewed without sugar	75	310	1.0	0	20.0	50.0	0	0	1.5	80	0.04	0.08	0.7	0
350 Puffed wheat breakfast cereal	325	1360	14.0	1.3	68.5	2.5	0	25	4.6	0	0	0.06	5.2	0
351 Pumpkin, raw	15	60	0.6	0	3.4	95.0	0	40	0.4	300	0.04	0.04	0.4	5
352 Quiche Lorraine	400	1670	15.0	28.0	20.0	35.0	600	250	1.0	150	0.10	0.20	1.0	0
353 Rabbit, stewed (with bones)	90	380	14.0	4.0	0	33.0	0	0	1.0	0	0.05	0.10	4.0	0
354 Radishes	15	60	1.0	0	3.0	93.0	60	45	1.9	0	0.04	0	0.2	25
355 Raisins	250	1050	1.0	0	65.0	21.0	50	60	1.5	0	0.10	0.08	0.5	0
356 Raspberies	25	100	1.0	0	6.0	83.0	0	40	1.2	15	0	0.03	0.4	25
357 Ready Brek breakfast cereal	390	1630	12.0	9.0	70.0	6.0	25	65	5.0	0	1.50	0.10	9.5	0
358 Red currants	20	80	1.0	0	4.0	83.0	0	40	1.0	15	0.04	0.06	0	40

per 100 g	Energy (kcal)	Energy (kJ)	Protein (g)	Fat (g)	Carb (g)	Water (g)	Sodium (mg)	Calcium (mg)	Iron (mg)	Vit A (µg)	Vit B₁ (mg)	Vit B₂ (mg)	Niacin (mg)	Vit C (mg)
359 Rhubarb, raw	5	20	0.5	0	1.0	94.0	0	100	0.4	0	0	0.03	0.3	10
360 Rhubarb, stewed with sugar	45	190	0.5	0	10.0	86.0	0	80	0.3	0	0	0.03	0.3	5
361 Rice Krispies breakfast cereal	350	1500	6.0	0.7	88.0	4.0	1300	0	7.0	0	1.00	1.50	16.0	0
362 Rice pudding, canned	90	380	3.5	2.5	15.0	77.0	50	100	0.2	30	0.03	0.15	0	0
363 Rice, white, raw	360	1510	6.5	1.0	87.0	12.0	0	0	0.5	0	0.10	0.03	1.5	0
364 Rice, white, boiled	120	500	2.0	0.3	30.0	70.0	0	0	0	0	0	0	0.3	0
365 Roe, cod, hard, fried	200	840	21.0	12.0	3.0	62.0	130	0	1.6	150	1.30	1.00	1.3	0
366 Roe, herring, soft, fried	240	1000	21.0	16.0	5.0	52.0	90	0	1.5	0	0.20	0.50	2.0	0
367 Sago, raw	360	1510	0.2	0.2	94.0	12.0	0	10	1.2	0	0	0	0	0
368 Salad cream see also Mayonnaise, number 268	300	1260	2.0	27.0	15.0	52.0	850	35	0.8	0	0	0	0	0
369 Salami	500	2090	19.0	45.0	2.0	28.0	2000	0	1.0	0	0.20	0.20	4.6	0
370 Salmon, raw	180	750	18.0	12.0	0	68.0	100	30	0.7	0	0.20	0.15	7.0	0
371 Salmon, canned	150	630	20.0	8.0	0	70.0	600	100	1.4	100	0.04	0.20	7.0	0
372 Salmon, smoked	140	590	25.0	5.0	0	65.0	2000	0	0.6	0	0.20	0.20	9.0	0
373 Salmon, steamed	200	840	20.0	13.0	0	65.0	100	30	0.8	0	0.20	0.10	7.0	0
374 Sardines canned in oil	220	920	24.0	14.0	0	58.0	650	550	2.9	0	0.04	0.40	8.0	0
375 Sardines canned in tomato sauce	180	750	18.0	12.0	0.5	65.0	700	460	4.6	0	0	0.30	5.5	0
376 Satsumas, peeled	35	150	1.0	0	8.0	87.0	0	40	0.3	15	0.07	0	0	30
377 Sauce, brown	100	420	1.0	0	25.0	64.0	1000	40	3.0	0	0	0	0	0
378 Sausage roll (flaky pastry)	500	2090	7.0	36.0	33.0	23.0	550	70	1.3	120	0.10	0.04	1.8	0
379 Sausage roll (short pastry)	460	1930	8.0	32.0	38.0	22.0	580	80	1.5	100	0.10	0.04	2.0	0
380 Sausage, liver sausage	300	1260	13.0	27.0	4.0	52.0	900	30	6.4	8000	0.20	1.60	4.0	0
381 Sausages, beef, raw	300	1260	10.0	24.0	12.0	50.0	800	50	1.4	0	0.03	0.10	5.0	0
382 Sausages, beef, fried	270	1130	13.0	18.0	15.0	48.0	1000	65	1.6	0	0	0.10	7.0	0
383 Sausages, beef, grilled	270	1130	13.0	17.0	15.0	48.0	1000	70	1.7	0	0	0.15	4.0	0
384 Sausages, frankfurters	270	1130	10.0	25.0	3.0	60.0	1000	35	1.5	0	0.10	0.10	1.5	0
385 Sausages, pork, raw	370	1550	11.0	32.0	10.0	45.0	750	40	1.1	0	0.04	0.10	3.4	0
386 Sausages, pork, fried	320	1340	14.0	25.0	11.0	45.0	1000	60	1.5	0	0	0.20	4.4	0

per 100 g	Energy (kcal)	Energy (kJ)	Protein (g)	Fat (g)	Carb (g)	Water (g)	Sodium (mg)	Calcium (mg)	Iron (mg)	Vit A (µg)	Vit B₁ (mg)	Vit B₂ (mg)	Niacin (mg)	Vit C (mg)
387 Sausages, pork, grilled	320	1340	13.0	25.0	12.0	45.0	1000	50	1.5	0	0	0.20	4.0	0
388 Sausages, saveloys, boiled	260	1090	10.0	21.0	10.0	57.0	900	25	1.5	0	0.10	0.10	2.0	0
389 Scampi, fried in breadcrumbs	320	1340	12.0	18.0	29.0	39.0	400	100	1.1	0	0.10	0.10	1.3	0
390 Scones	370	1550	7.5	15.0	56.0	21.0	800	600	1.5	150	0	0.10	1.2	0
391 Semolina, raw	350	1470	11.0	2.0	77.5	14.0	10	20	1.0	0	0.10	0	0.7	0
392 Sherry, dry	115	480	0	0	1.4	—	0	0	0.4	0	0	0	0.1	0
393 Sherry, sweet	140	590	0	0	7.0	—	0	0	0.4	0	0	0	0.1	0
394 Shredded Wheat breakfast cereal	320	1340	10.5	3.0	68.0	7.5	0	40	4.0	0	0.30	0.05	4.5	0
395 Shrimps, boiled	120	500	24.0	2.5	0	63.0	4000	300	1.8	0	0.03	0.03	3.0	0
396 Skate, fried in batter	200	840	18.0	12.0	5.0	62.0	140	50	1.0	0	0.03	0.10	2.4	0
397 Soup, chicken, canned	60	250	2.0	4.0	5.0	87.0	450	30	0.4	0	0	0	0	0
398 Soup, mushroom, canned	50	210	1.0	4.0	4.0	89.0	500	30	0.3	0	0	0	0.3	0
399 Soup, oxtail, canned	45	190	2.0	2.0	5.0	88.0	450	40	1.0	0	0	0	0.7	0
400 Soup, tomato, canned	60	250	1.0	3.0	6.0	84.0	450	0	0.4	60	0	0	0.5	0
401 Soup, vegetable, canned	40	170	2.0	1.0	7.0	85.0	500	0	0.6	0	0	0	0.4	0
402 Soya flour, full fat	450	1880	37.0	23.5	23.5	7.0	0	200	7.0	0	0.80	0.30	2.0	0
403 Soya flour, low fat	350	1460	45.0	7.0	28.0	7.0	0	240	9.1	0	0.90	0.40	2.4	0
404 Spaghetti, raw	380	1590	14.0	1.0	84.0	10.0	0	25	1.2	0	0.15	0.06	2.0	0
405 Spaghetti, boiled	120	500	4.0	0.3	26.0	72.0	0	0	0.4	0	0	0	0.3	0
406 Spaghetti, canned in tomato sauce	60	250	1.7	0.7	12.0	83.0	500	20	0.4	0	0	0	0.3	0
407 Special K breakfast cereal	360	1500	19.0	1.0	73.0	2.7	1000	50	13.0	0	1.20	1.70	18.0	0
408 Spinach, boiled	30	130	5.0	0.5	1.5	85.0	120	600	4.0	1000	0.10	0.15	0.4	25
409 Spirits (gin, vodka, whisky, etc)	220	920	0	0	0	—	0	0	0	0	0	0	0	0
410 Sponge pudding	340	1420	6.0	16.0	46.0	28.0	300	200	1.0	200	0	0.10	0	0
411 Sprats, fried	440	1840	25.0	38.0	0	34.0	130	700	4.5	na	na	na	na	na
412 Spring greens, boiled	10	40	1.7	0	1.0	94.0	0	90	1.3	1000	0.10	0.20	0.5	30
413 Steak, stewed, canned	180	750	15.0	13.0	1.0	70.0	400	0	2.1	0	0	0.10	2.4	0
414 Strawberries, fresh	25	100	0.5	0	6.0	88.0	0	20	0.7	5	0	0.03	0.4	60

	Energy (kcal)	Energy (kJ)	Protein (g)	Fat (g)	Carb (g)	Water (g)	Sodium (mg)	Calcium (mg)	Iron (mg)	Vit A (µg)	Vit B₁ (mg)	Vit B₂ (mg)	Niacin (mg)	Vit C (mg)
415 Suet, shredded see also Dripping, number 164 and Lard, number 234	830	3470	0	87.0	12.0	1.0	0	0	0	50	0	0	0	0
416 Suet pudding	300	1260	4.0	18.0	41.0	36.0	500	250	1.0	20	0	0.06	0.6	0
417 Sugar	390	1630	0	0	100.0	0	0	0	0	0	0	0	0	0
418 Sugar Puffs breakfast cereal	350	1470	6.0	0.8	84.0	2.0	0	15	2.1	0	0	0.03	2.5	0
419 Sultanas	250	1050	2.0	0	65.0	18.0	50	50	2.0	0	0.10	0.08	0.5	0
420 Swedes, raw	20	80	1.0	0	4.0	91.0	50	60	0.4	0	0.10	0.04	1.2	25
421 Swedes, boiled	20	80	1.0	0	4.0	92.0	0	40	0.3	0	0.04	0.03	0.8	20
422 Sweet potato, raw	90	380	1.0	0.6	22.0	70.0	0	0	0.7	700	0.10	0.06	0.8	25
423 Sweet potato, boiled	85	360	1.0	0.6	20.0	72.0	0	0	0.6	700	0.10	0.05	0.6	15
424 Sweetbread, raw	130	540	15.0	8.0	0	76.0	75	0	1.7	0	0.03	0.30	3.7	20
425 Sweetbread, fried with egg	230	960	19.0	15.0	6.0	60.0	200	35	1.8	0	0.03	0.25	2.0	18
426 Sweetcorn, canned	80	330	3.0	0.5	16.0	73.0	300	0	0.6	40	0.05	0.08	1.2	5
427 Sweetcorn, kernels only	125	520	4.0	2.0	23.0	65.0	0	0	0.9	40	0.20	0.10	1.7	10
428 Sweets, boiled	330	1380	0	0	87.0	0	25	0	0.4	0	0	0	0	0
429 Tangerines, peeled	30	130	1.0	0	8.0	86.0	0	40	0.3	15	0.07	0	0	30
430 Tapioca, raw	360	1510	0.4	0.1	90.0	10.0	0	0	0.3	0	0	0	0	0
431 Toffees	430	1800	2.0	17.0	71.0	5.0	300	100	1.5	0	0	0	0	0
432 Tomato juice	15	60	0	0	3.0	93.0	230	0	0.5	80	0.06	0.03	0.7	20
433 Tomato ketchup	100	420	2.0	0	24.0	65.0	120	25	1.2	0	0	0	0	0
434 Tomatoes, raw	15	60	1.0	0	3.0	93.0	0	0	0.4	15	0.10	0.05	0.7	20
435 Tomatoes, canned	12	50	1.0	0	2.0	94.0	30	0	0.9	15	0.10	0.03	0.7	20
436 Tomatoes, fried see also Soup, number 400	70	290	1.0	6.0	3.0	87.0	0	0	0.5	15	0.10	0.04	0.7	10
437 Tongue, canned	200	840	16.0	17.0	0	64.0	1000	30	2.5	0	0.04	0.40	2.5	0
438 Tongue, pickled, boiled	290	1210	20.0	24.0	0	49.0	1000	30	3.0	0	0.06	0.30	4.0	0
439 Treacle, black	260	1090	1.0	0	67.0	29.0	100	500	9.0	0	0	0	0	0
440 Treacle tart	370	1550	4.0	14.0	61.0	21.0	350	70	1.5	70	0.10	0	0.7	0
441 Tripe, stewed	100	420	15.0	5.0	0	79.0	70	150	0.7	0	0	0.08	0	0
442 Trout, steamed	140	590	24.0	4.5	0	71.0	90	40	1.0	na	na	na	na	na

per 100 g	Energy (kcal)	Energy (kJ)	Protein (g)	Fat (g)	Carb (g)	Water (g)	Sodium (mg)	Calcium (mg)	Iron (mg)	Vit A (μg)	Vit B₁ (mg)	Vit B₂ (mg)	Niacin (mg)	Vit C (mg)
443 Tuna, canned in oil	190	790	27.1	9.0	0	63.3	290	12	1.6	0	0.02	0.12	16	0
444 Turkey, raw (boned)	100	420	22.0	2.0	0	75.0	50	0	0.8	0	0.10	0.15	8.0	0
445 Turkey, raw (meat and skin)	145	610	21.0	7.0	0	72.0	50	0	0.8	0	0.10	0.10	7.0	0
446 Turkey, roast (boned)	140	590	29.0	3.0	0	68.0	60	0	0.9	0	0.10	0.20	8.5	0
447 Turkey, roast (meat and skin)	170	710	28.0	6.5	0	65.0	50	0	0.9	0	0.10	0.20	7.0	0
448 Turnips, raw	20	80	0.8	0	4.0	93.0	60	60	0.4	0	0.04	0.05	0.6	25
449 Turnips, boiled	14	60	0.7	0	2.0	95.0	30	60	0.4	0	0.03	0.04	0.4	20
450 Veal cutlet, fried in breadcrumbs	220	920	31.0	8.0	4.0	55.0	110	0	1.6	0	0.10	0.20	7.0	0
451 Veal fillet, raw	100	420	21.0	3.0	0	75.0	110	0	1.2	0	0.10	0.25	7.0	0
452 Veal fillet, roast	230	960	32.0	12.0	0	55.0	100	0	1.6	0	0.06	0.30	7.0	0
453 Veal, jellied, canned	130	540	25.0	3.0	0	69.0	1200	0	1.5	0	0.05	0.30	6.0	0
454 Venison, roast	200	840	35.0	6.0	0	57.0	90	30	8.0	na	na	na	na	na
455 Walnuts	530	2220	11.0	52.0	5.0	23.0	0	60	2.5	0	0.30	0.15	1.0	0
456 Watercress	14	60	3.0	0	0.7	91.0	60	220	1.6	500	0.10	0.10	0.6	60
457 Watermelons	20	80	0.5	0	5.0	95.0	0	0	0.3	0	0	0	0	5
458 Weetabix breakfast cereal	340	1420	11.5	3.5	70.0	3.8	360	30	7.6	0	1.00	1.50	12.0	0
459 White currants	30	120	1.5	0	6.0	83.0	0	20	1.0	0	0.04	0.06	0	40
460 Whitebait, fried in flour	530	2220	20.0	48.0	5.0	24.0	230	900	5.0	0	0	0	0	0
461 Whiting, fried in breadcrumbs	190	800	18.0	10.0	7.0	63.0	200	50	0.7	0	0.10	0.20	2.0	0
462 Whiting, steamed	90	380	21.0	1.0	0	77.0	130	40	1.0	0	0.10	0.20	3.0	0
463 Wine, red	70	290	0	0	0	—	0	0	1.0	0	0	0	0	0
464 Wine, white, dry	65	270	0	0	0.6	—	0	0	0.5	0	0	0	0	0
465 Wine, white, sweet	100	420	0	0	6.0	—	0	0	0.6	0	0	0	0	0
466 Yam, raw	130	540	2.0	0	32.0	73.0	0	0	0.3	0	0.05	0	0.5	2
467 Yam, boiled	120	500	1.5	0	30.0	66.0	0	0	0.3	0	0.05	0	0.5	2
468 Yoghourt, flavoured	80	330	5.0	1.0	14.0	79.0	60	170	0	0	0.05	0.25	0	0
469 Yoghourt, natural	50	210	5.0	1.0	6.0	86.0	80	180	0	0	0.05	0.30	0	0
470 Yorkshire pudding	200	840	7.0	10.0	26.0	56.0	600	130	1.0	40	0.10	0.20	0.6	0

Additions

per 100 g	Energy (kcal)	Energy (kJ)	Protein (g)	Fat (g)	Carb (g)	Water (g)	Sodium (mg)	Calcium (mg)	Iron (mg)	Vit A (µg)	Vit B₁ (mg)	Vit B₂ (mg)	Niacin (mg)	Vit C (mg)

Specimen calculation of a day's intake

food	portion	energy kJ	protein g	fat g	vit A μg	iron mg
Breakfast						
cornflakes	1 oz (30 g)	105	2.4	0.2	0	2.1
milk	5 fl oz (140 ml)	*				
sugar	2 tsp (12 g)	*				
bread	2 slices (60 g)	576	4.7	1.0	0	1.0
butter	15 g	471	0	12.3	150	0
coffee	cup	0	0	0	0	0
milk	1 fl oz (30 ml)	*				
*total milk	6 fl oz (170 ml)	111	5.6	6.5	85	0
sugar	1 tsp (6 g)	*				
*total sugar	18 g	293	0	0	0	0
Total breakfast		1547 = 368 kcal	12.7	20	235	3.1
Mid-morning						
bread roll	30 g	378	3	2.1	0	0.5
cheddar cheese	15 g	60	3.9	5.1	60	0
butter	5 g	157	0	4.1	50	0
black coffee	cup	0	0	0	0	0
Total mid-morning		595 = 141 kcal	6.9	11.3	110	0.5
Lunch						
tomato soup	150 ml	375	1.5	4.5	90	0.6
fried cod fillet	6 oz (170 g)	1207	35.7	13.6	0	2.0
chips	5 oz (140 g)	1470	5.6	15.4	0	1.3
lemonade	200 ml	160	0	0	0	0
Total lunch		3213 = 764 kcal	42.8	33.5	90	3.9

food	portion	energy kJ	protein g	fat g	vit A μg	iron mg
Evening meal avocado	100 g	920	4	20	15	1.5
roast beef	5 oz (140 g)	1176	37.8	16.8	0	3.6
boiled potatoes	6 oz (170 g)	561	2.4	0	0	0.5
sprouts	4 oz (110 g)	88	3.3	0	66	0.6
apple	120 g	180	0.2	0	0	0.2
Total evening meal		2925 = 696 kcal	47.7	36.8	81	6.4
Total for day		8279 = 1971 kcal	110.1	101.6	516	13.9
Rounded off		8300 = 2000 kcal	110	100	520	14

Sample questions

1 Calculate the cost of 50 g of protein from the cheapest and most expensive cuts of meat, the cheapest and most expensive fish, bread, and baked beans.

2 Calculate the energy, protein, and iron provided by each of the following snacks:
(i) a cheese sandwich (60 g wholemeal bread, 30 g cheese, 15 g margarine)
(ii) 150 g fish fingers (half crumbs, half fish) and 100 g chips
(iii) 150 ml tomato soup, 50 g bread roll, and 10 g margarine.

3 Calculate the contribution towards the daily intake of energy, protein, iron, calcium, vitamin A and vitamins B_1 and B_2 from a salad composed of: 50 g lettuce, 50 g tomato, 25 g beetroot, 25 g cucumber, and 25 g onion. Calculate the effect of adding 25 ml salad cream.

4 How much protein can be bought for 50p from (a) the cheapest variety of meat, (b) white bread, (c) boiled haricot beans, (d) beef sausages, (e) potato chips?

5 How much energy can be bought for 25p from the foods listed in question 4?

6 Supply a reasonable day's menu that would provide a total of (a) 750 µg vitamin A, (b) 1.5 mg vitamin B_1, (c) 2 mg vitamin B_2, (d) 10 mg iron.

7 Weigh all the foods you eat for a day and calculate the energy and nutrients consumed.

8 Estimate from memory the amounts of foods you ate yesterday, and calculate the energy and nutrients provided.

9 Design a snack meal and a traditional meal of meat and two vegetables and compare their contents of energy and nutrients.

10 Examine the labels of a number of packaged foods that you can find and calculate the respective prices per 1000 kcal and per 50 g of protein.

11 From the list of foods that you consumed in one day, as in question 7, modify your day's diet so as to increase each of the nutrients by (a) 15% and (b) 30%, without changing the energy intake.

12 From the list of foods that you consumed in one day, as in question 7, modify your diet so that it supplies only 1200 kcal, while the nutrients remain at the same level as usual. Express the amounts of the nutrients per 1000 kcal (ie, nutrient density).

13 Tables of food composition are often used in planning diets. What nutrients are important when looking up the nutritive value of chicken, potatoes, bread, cabbage, and egg? (Royal Society of Health, Diploma in Nutrition).

14 A family of four (mother, father, and twin boys of 12) are going away for the weekend in their caravan. Devise a menu and list the weights of foods they should take with them. (RSH Diploma).

15 Compare the nutritional values of skimmed milk and whole milk; cottage cheese and Cheddar cheese; margarine and butter; chicken and beef; corned beef and sausages. (RSH Certificate).

16 Compile a traditional main meal for one person, stating portion sizes, and show how the fat content could be reduced by changing the ingredients. (Part question, RSH Diploma).

17 Name two foods rich in iron, vitamin C, vitamin A, and vitamin D. (Part question RSH Diploma). Name three groups of foods containing dietary fibre and give two examples of each group. Give useful sources of each of four B vitamins. (Part question RSH Diploma).

Thanks are due to the Royal Society of Health for permission to reproduce questions from their Certificate and Diploma examinations.